NUDGED...

also by the author;

Steven, K. (1996) *Dance on the Fiddle* [CD].
Steven, K. (2000) *Dances in the Wilds* [CD].
Steven, K. (2003) *The Fiddle Workshop* [CD].
Steven, K. (2006) *Ward 40* [CD].
Various (2012) *Crown Street Ceilidh* [CD].
Steven, K. (2020) *Karen Steven's New Scottish Fiddle Tunes* [Book].
Steven, K. (2022) *The Stroma Swelkie* [CD].

and featured in:
Various (1995) *The Nineties Collection – New Scottish Tunes in Traditional Style* [Book].
Edinburgh: The Hardie Press

Various (1999) *Heat the Hoose vol 1* [CD].
Edinburgh: Foot Stompin Records

Various (2003) *Caithness Connections* [VHS Video].
Turriff: Ross Records

Various (2004) *25 Years of The Caithness Junior Fiddlers* [CD].
Thurso: Birnam CD

Various (2010) *The Flying Scots* [DVD].
Wick: Pan Records

Various (2017) *The Aberdeen Collection* [Book].
Aberdeen: Aberdeen University Press

NUDGED...

*A journey from music career
to brain surgery and back again*

By Karen Steven

Independent Publishing Network

NUDGED...

Cover design and artwork, Kathryn Preston, Prestset Bureau
kathryn@prestset.co.uk

Typesetting and internal artwork, Stephen Duxbury, Prestset Bureau
stephen@prestset.co.uk

www.prestset.co.uk

Published by

Independent Publishing Network 2023

ISBN: 978-1-80352-680-5

www.karensteven.co.uk

karen@karensteven.co.uk

Please direct all enquiries to the author

Back Cover photography by John Baikie

www.johnbaikiephotography.com & johnbaikiephoto@gmail.com

Although this publication is designed to provide accurate information in regard to the subject matter covered, the publisher and the author assume no responsibility for errors, inaccuracies, omissions, or any other inconsistencies herein. This publication is meant as a source of valuable information for the reader, however, it is not meant as a replacement for direct expert assistance. If such level of assistance is required, the services of a competent professional should be sought.

Printed in Scotland by Bell & Bain Limited

In memory of Anne, my nudger

and

for Wendy,

both inspiring and hard-working

dependable, high achievers,

consistent, no matter what,

loyal and trustworthy,

and, there for me

Lucky me! Thank you, both xoxo

Table of Contents

Foreword

It was the fiddle that brought Karen and I together in 1988. I was a practicing physician who was also deeply engaged in the Valley of the Moon Scottish Fiddle Camp (VOM), led by the great Scottish fiddler Alasdair Fraser and held near San Francisco, California. I was an aspiring fiddler also. My wife and I helped establish a financial aid program for the camp attendees that was particularly interested in bringing in talented youth from Scotland to interact with the cadre of young local players who attended our camp. All were students of traditional Scottish fiddle music. Into this environment came a very accomplished award winning 19-year-old player from Caithness, Scotland, Karen Steven. She had a distinctive style of playing that was rhythmically grounded and joyful to listen and dance to, and it did not hurt that she was a very accomplished performer and much admired.

As a cardiologist in Berkeley, California I dealt with many patients of all ages who encountered a sudden critical illness, often life threatening and life changing as a result of its impact. I followed patients over many years, witnessing the aftermath of the original illness that often extended well beyond any residual physical disability. Dealing with anxiety and fear of recurrence is common and managing these symptoms is key to full recovery. I have been acutely aware that each individual story brings insight and an experience and sharing the experience often gives others comfort and encouragement. Knowing that one is not alone is so important and sharing how it was dealt with brings comfort and an approach to recovery. In the author's case the end result brings hope, an essential ingredient for living a full and productive life.

Karen brings to the story the personal experience of going through a life- threatening sub arachnoid bleed from a cerebral aneurism at the age of 36. She suffered the shock of it and the full physical and emotional impact. Then, slowly and piece by piece, she put her physical, musical and emotional life back together. It took time and the tincture of time was an important therapeutic element. The return to her musical life seems to be the barometer that tells us that she did succeed. It took diligent research and study on her part, excellent medical care, strong support of family and friends, and a push from the supportive musical community for healing to be achieved.

We California fiddlers who have known Karen are thrilled by her come back. I expect that after reading this book that you will be too.

Pate D Thomson MD, FACC

Preface

Writing a book wasn't in my plan. Who would want to hear what I have to say? You have more chance of a bleed on the brain than winning the lottery. There's a one in 7-10,000 risk for brain bleed. I had one. Thankfully, just the one. You have a small chance of surviving a burst aneurysm. That was me too. Let me describe how it felt. I was thrust into the darkness of unconsciousness and woke to the news in hospital, I'd suffered a burst aneurysm, a massive bleed. I was alert enough to remember all my family members who had succumbed to the same. At the time, my music career had been thriving. I had established myself as a good fiddle player, a great fiddle teacher. I had been transitioning to include performance around that time too. My world crashed down around me, Thursday 20th October 2005. Six days later, I underwent surgery to repair the torn artery. Then began my road to recovery.

Just as the lights had gone out on 20th October when I had suffered the subarachnoid haemorrhage (SAH), out they went again. I'd lost all love for playing and teaching fiddle. No music therapy for me. Better find a new job. I deliberated for eight months. Decision made. That was it. Fiddle no more. Excited to retire from music, but nervous at the same time, I wondered what might replace fiddle in my life. After exploring medical administration for the NHS and roles in supply chain for an oil and gas services company, there was a curiosity in the back of my mind. My dear friend, Anne Taylor would often try to nudge me back to playing fiddle again. For a while, I resisted. From time to time, I relented. I borrowed a fiddle and played some gigs with Anne. I explored a bit of teaching again. The bottom line was, I admitted a relief to be once again playing and teaching fiddle, this time on a freelance basis.

It's taken me 16 years to complete my story. I've come full circle. Returning to a career in music has caught me out. I am happy with it. I want to share my personal brain injury experience with readers and fill in the gaps that the textbooks can't. Organ donation? I think I am comfortable with that now. Finding the charity, Headway UK was cathartic, the cushion of support my weakened head needed. I am delighted you are coming on my journey. This is my story, in my own words. Come and delve into it. No pity, please and no tears. I am happy to have; survived, endured, given up and started over.

Introduction

Better than winning the lottery, way better. A bit of short-term pain after the operation, nothing a few painkillers wouldn't sort out. And, the scar, a very neat and tidy souvenir, invisible most of the time. The tiniest of sensitivity, itch, where the sutures around the ear were, only very occasionally. No complaints, so carefully stitched. Given the statistics for morbidity and mortality after SAH, I was incredibly lucky. It's indescribable how utterly overwhelmingly amazing it feels to have recovered. I am a survivor and I owe my life to my Mr Currie, the neurosurgeon. My family and friends are a close second. They are the driving force who gave me the will to fight, the strength to get better. Life has become richer. Each day is more special than before. The world a better place. Colours appear more vivid, textures more varied. I've grown as a person, I think, like flowers in Spring. I am thankful for each precious day. That second chance at life, wonderful. Could so easily have had a different ending. Life could have been swiped away from me. I want to be a better person. I would like the lives of others to be more fulfilled. I want to give back to those who have supported and cared for me, in my great time of need. I find myself checking for the scar, scrutinising, is it still there? Of course, yes. It's very neat. I remember, 20 stitches, a question mark shape, directly above my right eye, straight back and around, down in front of my right ear. I have to try hard to see it. I remember the young, male medic, removing the stitches. I think, his first time. Very careful. Did a fantastic job. I still feel where the burr holes were, the initial holes, before the surgeon joined the dots using the craniotome (special saw) to remove the skull flap. There's no pigment in the skin where the drain was. For 24 hours, the drain remained in place, allowing excess fluid to be removed. 6 months it took, for that area to heal over. Weekly visits to my Thurso, GP to remove granulation and apply silver nitrate did the trick. I am so observant, so inquisitive. I hope I am not freaking you out as I pour over the details of my illness? A little obsessively curious, I believe it is best to be informed. They say, what doesn't kill you, makes you stronger. In the beginning, it was too soon for me to believe that. In some ways, I feel stronger. I survived the brain bleed that would engulf me for a while. It can quickly and unexpectedly get you; I know. Knowledge is weakness, I think. I am on edge, scared to trust that I am safe. I'm not sure there's anything that can be done to prevent a bleed. You can look after your health with a good diet and exercise, no smoking or drinking and try to eliminate stress. But, if you have a potential for a weakness in an artery, you might delay the onset, the development of an aneurysm. If you are lucky, it won't burst in your lifetime. Strange, mine burst, AND I feel lucky. In so many ways.

What am I grateful for? My SAH happened after my visit to Canada, not while I was there. I had forgotten to take out travel insurance. Imagine? Will try to make sure that doesn't happen again. I am grateful that John was on shift at the gym that night. John and colleagues looked after me so well, until I was handed over to the ambulance crew. By then I was unconscious. I am grateful for my family and great friends. I am so thankful for kind neighbours who phoned and left messages of support. Visits from mates in Caithness while I recovered, were a lifesaver. Musician friends continued to care about me, in spite of my giving up playing fiddle. Such a weight off my shoulders, at the time, giving up my music career.

It was a cold, dark, windy, autumn evening in the remote, far north of Scotland. Can you imagine the feeling of blood, curdling inside your head, and then, pop, something burst? Can you relate to a dizzying chill, on the back of a boiling rush and pop in your mind? Can you visualise the blackness of a deep cavern, speckled with thousands of tiny, shiny, red bubbles, as you struggle to remain conscious? The inspiration for the book cover. Would you panic, if you became breathless, as though every ounce of oxygen was being drained from your weakening body? How would you feel? Might you be afraid, as your voice became an incomprehensible whisper, before all the lights went out? Would you be gripped by terror when you came round in the ambulance, only to be sick, and sick again? Might you be grateful to black out again, not knowing whether there would be a next time to come round, that you might, or might not, wake up? Having no memory for the unconsciousness, would that be the more comfortable place to be? As I struggled to breathe, why did I refuse oxygen? Would oxygen have increased by blood pressure and caused further bleeding within the brain? Did the lack of oxygen keep me safer, I wonder, at least in the short-term?

What was I afraid of? Might oxygen have exacerbated the problem? Would your suppressed heart rate and blood pressure go dangerously high when the doctor leant over your hospital bed and calmy announced, 'We think you've had a SAH'? How would you know the best way to react? Panic was my natural reaction to such terrifying news. Would your physical body go into survival mode? Might your emotional side, crumble with the mental strain of taking in this foreign information? These things happen to other people, not me. The CT or MRI scan, I don't remember which, confirmed the suspected diagnosis, SAH. I was prepped for transfer to the nearest neurosurgical ward. Morphine had been administered throughout the previous night, apparently. I don't recall asking for it although my medical notes confirm that I did, repeatedly. There was a commode beside my hospital bed. Use that, they said. Ok, so Raigmore were considering it safe for me to get out of bed. That would contradict the rules at Aberdeen Royal Infirmary (ARI) where I was soon to be heading. After a bleed on the brain, and before repair, it's essential to remain horizontal, for safety reasons. Can't risk a second bleed when the first one isn't repaired. It would be like trying to reinflate an already burst balloon.

Prologue

There's a book in each one of us? For sure, there is. Get writing, I thought. Why not? Subject matter: traditional music career, acquired brain injury and music career crash. Would that work, I wondered? I will let you; the reader decide. I started writing, July 2007. It's taken a while, you must be thinking? I let the words pour out onto the page. I'd never written anything before, except for writing music. I must have written about 100 tunes by now. With a vivid memory of the event that had occurred 2 years earlier, I put pen to paper. My mind weighed down by flashbacks, I prayed. If the episode was in print, I could forget reliving the event. I could stop encouraging the flashbacks. I could refer to my writings to quench my refresh thirst. I would never forget the incident. With hard copy story filed away, my mind would be free to focus on living. To be free of the head clutter was the goal. Now, here it is, my story of life-threatening illness, sandwiched between a couple slices of music life. Actually, I don't know. I thought it doesn't come much scarier than brain surgery, and then…but that's another story. I will stick with this one, for now. Living daily with the fallout, the aftermath after being fixed, patched up in hospital was standard. Apologies, I don't mean to be disrespectful. Patched up? No. The scar, so neat, smooth and delicate. I had to look closely to see the stitches. Fixed? No, minutely focused and highly skilled neurosurgery. Within a few short months, I recovered physically from the surgery. The emotional trauma of the illness still lingered. Thoughts of having a recurring SAH were never far from my mind. They are still close, but not quite at the forefront. I'm not sure how often these days. By writing the book, the flash backs are justifiable, yes? People are subjected to trauma, diagnosed with serious, life threatening conditions every day. Was I any different? No. Why should I be? Look at Karen Darke, so strong and positive in life, on the back of her life-changing accident. On the brink of death, after severing her spine while rock climbing, Karen Darke has faced an incredible journey of achievement. When not conquering the toughest mountains and longest rivers, hand-biking (she is paralysed from the chest down), Karen Darke wins Paralympic medals – Silver in London 2012, Gold in Rio 2016, both for H1-2 road time trials. In the face of such adversity, Karen Darke has achieved so much more than many able-bodied do in a lifetime. When not working out in her wheelchair, Karen Darke writes. Her books are massively inspiring to read. Her motivational speeches compelling. Her ability to achieve, never hindered by her paralysis. What a treat, to hear her give a talk in Inverness, Scotland once, where she was living at the time. Travelling at one stage to South America, she trusted a spirit doctor to perform anaesthetic-free surgery on her back. Would she regain her mobility? Sadly no. Get up, she did though, dusting herself off. In all the ways she knows how, Karen Darke continues to impress; hand-biking, kayaking, pulling herself up El Capitan, a vertical rock formation in California. Her resilience and strength of character are enviable. Her belief in the unbelievable quite incredible. Her stamina and achievements astounding.

Like myself, Australian actress and singer, Kylie Minogue was struck down by life-threatening illness in 2005. Despite a diagnosis of breast cancer, Kylie has gone on to sell over 80 million recordings globally. Happy with my few thousand record sales following brain surgery in the same year, I have nothing but admiration for the feisty Minogue. Adding to her mammoth record sales, Kylie also has multiple, significant accolades for acting and music. This speaks of someone who is living life, not simply existing. Kylie, clearly grabbed the bull by the horns, picking up from where she left off, prior to illness. More than happy, I have memories of coming 1st at Caithness Music Festival for fiddle, 1st overall for Highland Dancing at Halkirk Highland Games, recipient of a few study scholarships to travel to Valley of the Moon Fiddle Camp,

California and Cape Breton Island, Canada, plus some commissions – all for music, from Highland and Aberdeen Councils respectively.

At just 18, Australian singing sensation, Delta Goodrem faced her battle with life threatening, Hodgkin's lymphoma. Delta is gutsy and determined. With multiple number-one singles under her belt and a host of accolades for her music successes, Delta continued to release music, even while undergoing treatment for the cancer. Delta plugged the gaps of cancelled tours with new releases. Fans at the forefront of her mind, concurrent with serious illness. What a star! The Delta Goodrem Foundation was established as recently as 2020. Showing no sign of slowing down, Delta's charity mission is to raise funds for blood cancer research. Delta frequently acknowledges the support of her many fans in aiding her recovery. I can't help but be inspired by Karen Darke, Kylie and Delta. All three remain successful, high achievers, survivors, with a great work ethic. They are my inspiration when I look for strength coping with my anxieties around brain bleed that persist in hanging around. Seeing this book in print is just one example of my reaching new goals. Am I proud? Yes. I had to be. In a way, it was an easy mission. I just hope that I can convert the effort into interest. I truly believe that one of my USPs (unique selling point) is the personal experience. By that, I mean confronting the brain haemorrhage story and sharing it with you. The multiple books and leaflets about SAH present all manner of potential side effects and symptoms. Not every patient will encounter them all. The side effects and symptoms come with varying levels of severity. I aim to give as much detail as I remember about my own experience. For other patients and for friends, family and carers of someone who has experienced a SAH, my focus will be on providing clarity. Knowledge is power? I think so. I hope to convey at times my coping mechanisms throughout recovery. I hope to empower and give confidence while at times acknowledge the seriousness of the condition. I won't pretend, having a SAH is a serious and life-threatening condition. You will be exposed to my, one understanding of it. I hope that on balance, my other themes will serve to offer perspective on for example, music, my first love.

I strike a balance. I dive in, headfirst, giving you my uplifting and positive experiences with music. I thrive on challenge. Why then, do I sometimes feel like a quitter? I gave up playing my fiddle. Can you understand that? It's like recognising I was good at it, yet casting it aside, like a worn out, old cloth. Something new, something different, almost anything but music, drawing me in. Out with my control, I gave in to the voice. But, not instantaneously, you see. Careful consideration, taken over time.

My journey begins the day I suffered the SAH. In revealing what I remember of the experience I aim to portray the NHS neurosurgical team as an extremely caring and efficient workforce. I go on to explain that my own chosen former career path was a joy. Music didn't feel like work. I was in the enviable position of doing something I loved for a living. The dedicated staff in Ward 40, neurosurgery, Aberdeen have a similar life ethic. Not once did I witness a lethargic, disinterested member of staff. I have no complaints. When I was cold, they brought me blankets. When I was in pain, they supplied the morphine. They were caring, sensitive and scrupulous. They helped, advised and kept me as comfortable as possible. At no time were visitors turned away. I hope the quality of your healthcare experiences match mine. Providing feedback to healthcare providers, I think, is vitally important. Recognise excellent care, not just when there's a pandemic. Communicate opinions through the right channels. The website www.careopinion.org.uk offers an excellent sounding board for feedback. Good feedback is encouraged. They are open to suggestions for improvements to the health service. The site can be used to give thanks for care. In return, prompt replies indicate statistics on stakeholder numbers and departments, who have read and engaged with your messages. Use the service to communicate with care professionals. Tell them what you think. You really will be communicating with actual people, and not receive computer generated auto responses.

My relationship with close friends and family became stronger. I could feel it, during and after my SAH. I have mixed feelings of strength and weakness, strength in that I managed to endure the haemorrhage, weakness, in questioning will I survive it next time? I feel vulnerable and fragile, somehow flawed. At the same time, I feel special, unique in a way. I can't help but feel a little guilty at times. I survived when there are so many who are less fortunate than me. 25% of SAH sufferers die immediately. A further 25% die on the way to hospital. Of the remaining 50%, neurological deficit is a risk. Others will die, waiting for, or during surgery. Stroke by blood clot is a risk after brain bleed. Do you see? Lucky me, yes. I survived all of that. I had no long-lasting memory impairment. Speech and mobility issues were nonexistent for me. There's my strength. For a moment, I return to feeling as I did before the haemorrhage, invincible. Experience tells me not to be flippant. Precaution is needed, to help prevent a recurring, burst aneurysm. Bizarrely I feel an urge to tell people my story. Subconsciously, perhaps for therapeutic release and reaction from listeners. The flip side of the concerns I had were balanced by the confidence I had to return to work, though to a different job. Brain injury support group, Headway Highland were invaluable to me, once my driver's licence was returned. Members share their brain injury experience. Listening is key. Openness and trust within the group comes naturally. Each relates to one another's burdens. Through perseverance I found the medical intervention I had been looking for to tackle the psychological issues associated with the trauma of the brain injury. While the underlying theme of the book is the brain injury, I discuss family in the context of the haemorrhage, career change and a positive outlook. I turned my back on my first love, the fiddle. I aim to justify that.

I celebrate my fiddle story with you. Let me share my most treasured memories of fiddle playing, fiddle teaching. I bring you my brain injury story. I relive the six months recovery period before returning to work. Witness the flashbacks to the night 'it' happened. In them, I look for warning signs that the SAH was about to get me. I describe the exhaustion that engulfed me. I recount the near collapse as I struggled to get help.

Critical illness cover? What was that? At age 31, I didn't see the relevance to me. Too young for trauma. The small addition to my monthly mortgage repayment would be a life saver of a different kind. The insurance policy was mandatory with my chosen lender. Had the cover been optional I feel certain I would have declined the extra monthly expense. Once again, lucky me! Thought I was invincible, immune almost to these dangers. I thought these challenges are faced by other people. And, then out of the blue, it did happen to me. Hindsight tells me, recommend everyone should get cover, should find the little extra each month for illness insurance. You simply never know when you might need to rely on it. Pause for a moment. Think about TV presenter, Jonnie Irwin, 'A Place in the Sun'. Jonnie is terminally ill. He has no Critical Illness Insurance. Such a painful story. With a wife and three young children, Jonnie must continue to work, whilst undergoing treatment for aggressive cancer. Imagine, that could be you. Can you imagine, not affording to focus on recovery from illness? Can you imagine, you are sick, seriously sick, but you have to keep working? I urge all of you, if you don't have critical illness insurance, please make sure you get some. I wonder, could it be made mandatory, like vehicle insurance? The right kind of illness cover, is an insurance policy, should the terrible happen. These days however, can I find a new cover policy? Not really, actually, Insurance providers are not willing to do that. You see, the medical world sees me as treated, permanently fixed, safe. The insurance world? They see me as too much of a risk. These conflicting messages added to my confusion and anxiety as I tried to believe I was safe. Recovery hampered when insurance companies turned me down. How could my anxiety subside? I found, when I was vulnerable, the surgeon said I was safe while insurance companies said I was too risky. You see, I was scared, even more so when insurance companies would not offer me a policy. Too traumatised to stand up for myself, I receded. The confidence to pick myself up, knocked. I wanted to focus on recovery, by that time, my emotional recovery. In the book, I don't dwell on the negativity of being unable to get or afford insurance. When travelling these days, I am resigned to cover, except for pre-existing conditions. Therefore, cover for brain bleed is excluded for me. The strong me tells myself, I'm good, that's fine, I'm comfortable without cover for brain bleed. But where is that mantra, during the night, when I wake, feeling vulnerable again?

I bring you my story about making a CD of Scottish fiddle and guitar music. It was a fundraiser for the neurosurgery ward at ARI. I highlight the project was about the hospital and not about me. It makes a refreshing change. Promoting a charity is a more comfortable place than self-promotion. At times essential, blowing your own trumpet is not easy. It comes with the territory of being a musician for a living, however. I just wasn't comfortable taking that level of care. Instinctively, I felt the need to repay the NHS for my operation and care. In doing so, I leant on some people to bring the project to fruition. Thankful for their support in my mission, my team were focused, driven and on my side.

What was my ideal? Overcoming fear of recurring SAH in the first instance. Secondly, was a quest to gain knowledge of the condition. Those closest to me, including professionals, preferred I was less obsessed with how aneurysms develop, the treatment options and prognosis. I have tried to limit my reading to; two textbooks on neurosurgery, an 864 page, academic pocket book on clinical medicine and a few websites. In addition, I have discussed SAH with; other survivors, my surgeon, my neuropsychologist and trained specialists at www.brainandspine.org.uk. I am a firm believer in being fully informed. Some people prefer not to know the gory details of surgery. I respect that. I need to know. There's a thirst for the details. Armed with my list of queries, anxiety alleviated for a bit, when the medics respond. Comprehension diluted when the doctors are no longer there. Not an attractive place to be. Lying flat on my back in a hospital bed for two weeks, the morphine intervened. My sharpness of mind, dormant while my body fought to survive. Within a week or two of leaving hospital I began researching my condition.

I studied long and hard over many years to become a well-respected fiddle teacher. My standard of playing didn't come about overnight. I really struggled. I had little confidence in my ability as a musician for a long time. Meeting some people who would become great friends and a huge inspiration was like a turning point for me. Music was the tool I used, to communicate my emotions. The music on hold while I was in hospital, the morphine put its stamp on any free-flowing ability I had, at least about feelings. Ironically when the whole idea of really giving up my music came to a head, I was performing at a festival alongside two of these main supporters and sources of my musical inspiration; Alasdair Fraser and Jerry Holland. The journey I have been on since October 2005, educating myself and recovering from the biggest fright of my life coincided with another journey, the one where music went from meaning everything to me to a transition into pursuing other activities, dreams and pursuits. I explore some aspects of my fiddle world, putting them in context with the haemorrhage. I aim to portray how my life has been shaped since. In doing so, I celebrate all that excited me about the fiddle; the challenge of learning to play the instrument, core inspiration to play, the opportunities that arose for me over the years and the great music partnerships that fortified my zest for a musical life.

Why was I happy to let go of my music? I sometimes wonder. For certain, I feel, whatever career I had before my brain injury, I would have had to give it up to pursue something else. Was the choice mine? I don't believe so. The music life was taken from me, I'm sure. I don't ever feel my decision was about the music. It was about some powerful force within me. Was there a voice in my head? Yes, for sure. Remember what that voice said? No. It was a different voice. But, just like the voice that repeats the words SAH in my mind over and over, I was plagued by this other one. I became indifferent to the music, disrespectful of it, in a way. Snubbing the music, when so many others would jump at the chances I'd enjoyed. There was nothing I could do. I couldn't stop the feelings. I didn't want to. I was certain of that. I didn't push though, to try and keep playing. I allowed myself to give up. Frantically, I hoped for a replacement therapy, a different kind of busy. Whatever the voice was saying, the message was, start over, start afresh, engage in a new beginning. I wasn't going to mourn the loss of my fiddle dream. I wouldn't forget my music. I wouldn't forget how to play. Playing a musical instrument is like riding a bike. The music would always be there, be somewhere. The quality would be a little rusty, if I was to start over. I thought, if I feel the need to explore it again, it'll be there, waiting. I could try and pick up from where I left off. Why didn't my love for the fiddle, fuel my recovery? At the time, 2006, I was comfortable thinking about brain injury and emotional recovery from that.

On finding this book, I hope that readers can gain an insight into the life of someone who has had an acquired brain injury. I hope it provides other sufferers with the knowledge that it is possible to get better. I hope that carers of brain injured can learn that it is normal to feel anxiety, worry and panic after undergoing brain surgery. I aim to present my coping mechanisms in an attempt to show that I am living life. I fill my days with work and play and by stretching myself on a personal and professional level. In portraying many positives in my life following the SAH, I hope that other brain injured, their families and carers can see that there is light in life after brain injury. It is possible to live life rather than merely exist.

NUDGED...

Out of the Blue

I thought, it's inconceivable that this has happened. Things like this happen every day to someone, somewhere, but not me!? I felt as though my life was ebbing away. I struggled to breathe. It wasn't a choking feeling. Taking deep breaths was impossible. Taking a normal breath, I couldn't. It was like I was only getting wisps of oxygen. I could feel the unconsciousness approach. It took hold of me. There was nothing I could do. Were my eyes closed? I don't know. I remember everything going black. It was like looking into a deep, dark void. There was a swirling sensation. I was conscious enough to feel unnerved, in the beginning. Am I angry? Have I felt anger about the SAH? No, why would I? Why should I? I don't blame anyone or anything. Maybe that's easy to say because I survived. There's nothing to be gained by apportioning blame. At times it's as though I didn't endure any physical pain. You can relate to that, yes? Forgetting there ever has been pain, when it is no longer there, right? I feel strongly that I've had the best treatment. Why do I say that? I can't imagine any better care. You might think, if I was that unwell, maybe I wasn't in a position to judge. I know there are bigger hospitals. There are bigger teams of neurosurgeons in other places. For me, I only needed that one team.

Mr Currie, my neurosurgeon. He did the operation. He seemed old school. He had a perfect combination of skill, experience and empathy. A genuinely caring nature can be missing sometimes in medicine. Bedside manner is so important. Mr Currie had performed many operations on burst aneurysms. He was so focused. I felt valued. Mr Currie seemed revered on the ward. ARI is also a teaching hospital. Younger ward staff seemed to look up to him. Lucky them, lucky me. Back to the best care. Imagine it any better? No. Sometimes, it catches me unawares. The reality that it did happen. I remember the throwing up. Not often, a couple of times in the ambulance, at least once in A&E and then, I think, not until after my main operation. I remember discussions about surgery. I didn't fully comprehend the options. What were the options? Do nothing and risk a rebleed sooner or later or have traditional surgery in Aberdeen. Alternative treatments would cause further delay, and delays would add danger. I say options. There was just the one, in reality. With bed space at a premium, I was encouraged to accept traditional surgery in Aberdeen. No conservative keyhole procedure. I didn't appreciate the seriousness of traditional surgery. Afterwards, when I began to study all things aneurysm, I decided I was lucky, very lucky to have had the bigger, I think riskier surgery. I was perfectly satisfied to remain in ARI, and to not risk further deterioration by travelling to Edinburgh for the more conservative, keyhole procedure, coiling. I wonder if I was subconsciously gaining strength from my granny, bravery to undergo surgery, as she had done, on many occasions throughout her life. I believe that as her life was ebbing away, she somehow managed to pass on some of her strength to me. Physically, as the days passed, I was growing weaker. Granny was too. At the time, I didn't realise. Or, if I did, I couldn't remember. Fluids were being pumped into me by a drip. I had no desire to eat. Days passed without me craving anything. Friends, Anne and Wendy would coax me to eat the smallest piece of a fruit or teaspoonful of yoghurt. With the pain came lack of appetite. Yet, I allowed the doctors and nurses to prod me with needles and check my reflexes. I was strong in that sense and let them carry out the tests they needed to. I felt obliged to stay awake for visitors. The headaches prevented restful sleep. I had such kind visitors, doing their best to keep me company and offer support. Alongside mum, dad and sisters Pauline and Maree, I was grateful for regular visits from Anne, Wendy and Alison, not forgetting musician pal, Pete MacCallum and my university lecturer, Seumas Grant. My appetite was suppressed for the first time in my life, I think. Thank goodness I didn't have to swallow a tube like the poor patient in the bed next to me, who resisted and fought with the staff. This was another reason to feel lucky. It was as though granny was with me, every step of the way. I think she held on until after my operation, passing away only once she knew I could cope without her. At 93, granny passed away on 29th October 2005. My surgery had been on 26th October. I do believe she waited until she thought I was safe, post-op. It had been a fairly normal day, and then...I was snatched completely out of the blue, from my secure world.

I didn't suffer any warning headaches in the days leading up to my SAH. How lucky I was. Are pre-bleed headaches common? They can be. Having just returned from a holiday in Canada, which was drenched with my beloved Cape Breton fiddle music, with my friend Alison, the haemorrhage could have so easily happened out there. The infectious energy of the music called to us. Alison and I embarked on an inspirational trip to the Canadian Island that dripped with fiddle talent. I had completely forgotten to arrange travel insurance...never again! In some cases, warning headaches in the days before a SAH can be a symptom of impending rupture of a brain aneurysm. No pains for me, just, wall to wall fiddle music, fiddle heaven!

It had been a pretty average day, the day I suffered the haemorrhage. I knew I would only have one student that day. My remaining students had gone to a fiddle course in Beauly for the week. Renowned fiddle band Blazin' Fiddles stage a week-long event there every year in October. They provide high quality instruction by ear (without sheet music). Lots of would be, young (and young at heart) Blazers descend upon the idyllic Highland village in the heart of Ross-shire intent on capturing some of, in those days, Bruce, Catriona, Iain, Allan and Aidan's fiddle magic. The band, stars of the Scottish Fiddle scene hailed from all corners of Scotland from Shetland in the north to Inverness in the central Highlands and from Glenfinnan in the West to Seil Island in the Southwest. Their eclectic mix of individuality fitted tightly together. They complemented one another. They would spellbindingly embrace each other's native musical tongues. Each player in the band would be afforded a moment to shine individually before uniting, driving with great zeal towards gripping climaxes. Blazin' Fiddles audiences, always charmed, leaving fans yearning for more. That could have been me.

The inaugural performance of Blazin' Fiddles was in May 1998. Band leader, Bruce MacGregor invited me to join them. Unfortunately, there was a clash. My final degree exams were just around the corner. I was forced to make a choice; abandon degree to join the band or complete my degree and pass up the opportunity to join the newly formed Blazin' Fiddles. Nervous to walk away from my degree, the dilemma played on my mind. Imagine, Blazin' Fiddles might have been a one tour wonder. Imagine repeating 4th year university, had I walked away in the final hour of my degree. With difficulty, I declined Bruce's generous offer and went on to gain a 2:1 Hons degree in Gaelic Studies. I am delighted for Bruce. Blazin' Fiddles went on to be at the forefront of traditional Scottish fiddle music. Their impact cemented. To this day, they are still one of the most riveting bands on the traditional music scene. At the time, I was really torn. Should I have joined the band? Maybe. Four years of hard work. So close to the end. Always goal orientated, whether professional or personal. My degree was, first a personal goal and secondly would hopefully stand me in good stead professionally. Although primarily a Gaelic Studies course, taking an elective in psychology, I think, strongly contributed to me getting through my degree. While developmental psychology was interesting, I most enjoyed studying memory, which was a great benefit when it came to exams. Pursuing music as a solo artist and music teaching, after graduation, had turned out to be a safe option for me. One where I was in control, I was spared the many late nights faced by touring musicians. Can't do them. I'm a morning person. How many tours did I forego by not joining the Blazin' Fiddles band? How many great CDs might I have been on, if I chose the band over my degree? The running total of Blazin' Fiddles CDs currently stands at 9, not including a total of 3 tune books. Had I joined the band, might the SAH have occurred much sooner? I guess so. I'm a glass half full kind of person.

Then again, when it comes to SAH, I find myself considering anything to pin it on. Had I been a touring musician, might my body have been robust enough to withstand the effects of the haemorrhage? Maybe not. Satisfied with my choice to decline joining Blazin' Fiddles, the outcome in the long run, Lucky, lucky me! Torn at the time, on reflection, was the best decision.

Blazin' Fiddles went on to establish an annual, week-long fiddle course. Coinciding with the October Highland school holidays, the course landed during the first week of our college's winter term. As all except for one of my students had slipped away to attend the course, it was only fair for me to treat remaining student, Dana, to a day at the prestigious workshops with Blazin' Fiddles. Some unexpected work delays first. Then, we set off in search of some inspiration, Dana with fiddle and me my newly acquired cello. Dana and I met at the end of the day to devise a plan for the evening. A great fiddler from Unst, Shetland, Dana had volunteered to perform at the course concert in Beauly that night. I left for my keep fit class back home but agreed to return to Beauly later that evening to take Dana home.

I recall feeling quite shivery and tired that day. Unable to put my finger exactly on how I was feeling, I knew I wasn't immersed in the music like I normally would be. I wasn't feeling the music that day. I would normally crave and savour each moment. I was thrilled to see old musician friends; Sally, Mike, Pete and Christine and to make some new ones: I'm afraid I have forgotten their names. To an extent, I was simply busking along with the group. Strangely, I wasn't contributing energy to the sound. Usually so enthused and exhilarated by the music, I would naturally lead sessions in terms of drive and tempo. A head full of repertoire, I would normally, instinctively come up with tune after tune. Playing good music can often be a private experience, emotionally. It's so easy to form a connection with other inspirational players. You sense it, between you. It's an auditory experience. The audience won't always be aware. Good players subconsciously inspire each other. The phrasing, dynamics, harmonies and rhythm of the music can be exciting. Playing with a great musician, makes a good musician play better. There's visual interaction between players who are playing together. It's a public experience when the emotions of the musicians are visible to see. Although, a smile from me when I play, would often be a sign I've made a mistake. That day at the Blazin' in Beauly course, I didn't thrive on the experience. Instead, I had one of those there in body but not in spirit moments. I felt a little frustrated. I was numb to the environment. It was a strange sensation. I was puzzled, my mood flat. I was very aware of the feeling that day. Was something going on in my head at that time? Was my blood pressure rising? Did I experience a subconscious distraction from the music? Where was the excitement I would normally encounter with my music? Did it get diluted while my body's attention focused on the aneurysm that was going to rupture later that day?

If I dig around in my mind, I strain to find another example of a time when I felt so distant spiritually from my music. Music was my dream as I grew up. I had dreamt of making it as a musician. It seemed that only a few are lucky enough in the Scottish traditional music world to make a living from music. For a number of years, I thought a dream is how music would remain for me. Slowly and carefully, I built up a portfolio of work, gaining experience of teaching and learning, initially at Thurso College. I later progressed to teaching at annual summer schools, around the UK and Scandinavia. Yet, here I was in 2005 with a number of years' experience as a musician under my belt, feeling indifferent about it. It's quite ironic really to think I felt detached from the music immediately before my haemorrhage and ultimately, I experienced the same turmoil after the event, the only difference being that I felt it constantly afterwards.

I became disconnected from my music. They say music is a healer? Music is therapy, is it not? I can relate to that. I think I felt sluggish that day, all of that day in Beauly. I wonder, was my blood pressure going up while I felt lethargic and heavy? Hypertension may be the cause of an aneurysm developing. More than 50% of people experiencing a burst aneurysm have a history of high blood pressure. Strange, I thought, my blood pressure had always been on the low side of normal. I wonder, had my aneurysm been preparing to erupt that day? Whether aneurysms develop and burst within a few minutes or hours, or even days, weeks or months, is not known. A cerebral angiogram which is vital in determining the size and location of an aneurysm can rule out the presence of one today but is no guarantee that one will not begin to grow tomorrow. My surgeon Mr Currie reminded me of this when I discussed my concerns for other family members. My sister Pauline remains confident that she is safe. Of course, her children are the most important thing in her life. She says she cannot afford to be stressed or worry about aneurysms. They are so unpredictable, she said. Controlling blood pressure and cholesterol levels by reducing smoking, drinking and taking care of diet all serve to help minimise the risk of a haemorrhage. I always admire Pauline for her strength of character and belief. I'm certain that her positive mentality and attitude to life are good protectors.

I drove home to Alness after the day in Beauly and prepared to attend my Body pump, weightlifting class. I would lift a range of weights depending on the muscle group being worked at the time; 10kg for shoulder exercises, 20kg for back exercises. In contrast to this resistance class, I enjoyed Body Attack, which was high impact aerobics. Each lasting an hour, the classes ran back-to-back. I enjoyed the calorie burn from Body Attack.

I felt heavy with tiredness. It was only mid-October, but I shivered with cold. I hauled myself up from my comfortable sofa. If I pushed myself out the door, I would appreciate the benefits of a good workout from Body Pump. Thirty fit and toned bodies, hard from pumping iron at regular workouts, prepared their workload for the class ahead. Hard body? Not me, not yet, but working on it. I hovered around 64kg at the time but felt reasonably fit. The class assembled 20kgs of weight onto the bar. The music was loud, upbeat. The warmup began. I needed to warm up.

Like some sort of hostile volcano, without warning, the intense heat rumbled and bubbled, my head bursting. It happened so suddenly, the pop in my head. I managed not to drop the weight bar. I took my time, couldn't stumble and attract attention. But I felt the need to hurry. Setting the weight down, I staggered towards the exit. Worriedly, I sneaked away. My head didn't feel well. The music continued. The class carried on. I stumbled incoherently to the bathroom. I was alert enough at this stage to realise I was too frightened to go in. What if I collapsed, not to be found until it was too late? It was a strain making my way upstairs to the reception area. Thank goodness for my good friend John. He was on duty at reception that night. I stumbled towards John. I said I felt really unwell. Was I able to explain much at that stage? I don't know. I needed to sit down. I parked myself on the floor. Consumed with exhaustion, I lay on the floor. Come closer to the phone, John had said. The call handler needed to ask questions. In a few short moments, unable to speak beyond a whisper, I think I must have blacked out. After that, it was up to John, colleagues and the call handler to decide on the course of action.

Extremely worried when I first became ill, my gut feeling was that it was serious. Although surrounded by fitness centre staff, I felt quite alone. At times like that, you need your family. It was getting late. I didn't feel inclined to telephone my family and worry them, possibly unnecessarily. After being sick, twice in the ambulance and once in A&E, Raigmore Hospital, I drifted in and out of consciousness again. Strapped down on the trolley, to prevent me from falling out of the bed, I was still only able to whisper. This wasn't enough to be heard. The next thing I knew, I had woken from a blackout to see a pool of vomit on the floor. Figures huddled the other side of the curtain; I was unable to alert staff to my predicament. I blacked out again, not waking, to my knowledge, until the next morning, in a ward. I was so frightened when I heard Dr Steven in Raigmore say I'd had a SAH. A SAH is a type of stroke. I've read that 5% of strokes are of the SAH type. A third of brain aneurysms rupture during exercise. A burst aneurysm can get you, no matter how fit and strong you are. A healthy body, no guarantee you won't succumb to the nasty. And 70% of SAHs are as a result of burst aneurysm, my type. My immediate thought was of my aunt, my mum's sister who at 35 had had exactly that while working in the canteen at Wick High School. She never regained consciousness. Then there was my aunt's son Ian, my first cousin who also suffered a brain haemorrhage. Ian was just 30. He suffered the same fate. I couldn't get the thoughts of my aunt and cousin out of my mind. I didn't know the details, so as I lay in the hospital bed with what I believed to be the same thing I worried and waited for something else to happen, something more sinister...I don't even like to spell out my thoughts now in case of tempting some scary fate.

After an MRI scan in Raigmore hospital Inverness had confirmed the haemorrhage, Dr Steven told me I would be transferred to ARI, for what I didn't know at the time. I tried not to think about it although I could think of nothing else. My thoughts went from head surgery to bed rest and recuperating and back to surgery again - not really wanting to contemplate the enormity of what had happened and what was about to happen next. I began to imagine what would happen at ARI. I thought, would there be surgery? No, I discounted that. I wondered, was I going to the ARI for recovery? I didn't know. The two ideas floated around in my mind. I tried not to imagine having surgery. When I did contemplate it, I imagined the surgeon going in under my chin or through my neck, somewhere soft, a keyhole surgery, something less invasive. That's the modern way of surgery nowadays, isn't it? Eh, no, not always. It turned out I had been so naïve. Right up to the moment I was wheeled away to the theatre I never questioned the surgical procedure, how it would be carried out. There had not even been a mention of having my head shaved or performing a craniotomy (skull fracture). I can only imagine that by my age most people have some experience of surgery, either themselves or someone close to them. I guess at that time, I lacked an inquisitive nature. Children? No, don't have any. Fear of hospitals? Yes. Of course, now I was fully aware, no childbirth does not guarantee a hospital-free life.

I was prepared for the ambulance journey from Inverness to Aberdeen. The distance was around 100 miles. Not single track, but just one or two sections with dual carriageway. With no bypass roads around towns, there was no quick way to get there, frequently having to slow down to 30mph in towns along the way. I remember feeling calm. I had the company of the 2 paramedics, who took it in turns to drive/sit with me. I was given a dose of morphine. Until then, I don't remember complaining of a sore head, although my hospital records for the 14-hour period I was in Raigmore hospital, frequently state that I was in pain. It was as though I was suspended in a sense of lightness, airiness, floating, the effects of the morphine. Is there such a thing as being able to talk while unconscious? The paramedic who first sat with me on the journey to Aberdeen was quite young, in his early 20s I think. He was very good company. He freely discussed and explained my circumstances, telling me his wife had had a SAH when she was 23, I think. The way he described my condition was as though SAH was fairly common and routine which made me wonder why I thought it was so serious. I remember arriving at Ward 40 in Aberdeen and the same paramedic announcing this is the subarachnoid from Inverness. It seemed a little bit funny. Bizarre to remember such a comment and at the same time to forget so much else, like my uncle Dainie visiting. Hopefully I can be forgiven as I think he was there on the day of my surgery. He would have been a great support for my mum. I was placed on a waterproof bed. It was the morning of my operation. The nurse showered me, head to toe, washed my hair and gave me a blow dry. I have a vivid memory of that. We chatted, just normal small talk, I remember. Did it help, to calm me I mean? Yes, absolutely. I'm not sure I appreciated that morning to be any different really, than the others. Did I actually need to be calmed? At that time, I mean? I'm not sure. I was being pampered, right? The nurse, I remember her telling me, she used to be a hairdresser. Soon after, mum, dad and my sisters waved me off to theatre. The last image I have, before general anaesthetic (GA) is of mum, in the corridor, on her own. To have had so many family members suffer brain haemorrhage, the feeling for her must have been almost unbearable. There was nothing I could do. Normally so independent, both of us are, I/we quietly shared a moment. Silently. Did I raise my hand? Wave to mum? Did she wave back? I'm not sure. Mum was incredible. Brave, always has been. And there she was again, when I came round. The side effects of the GA brought on the next wave of sickness. Small price to pay for a life-saving operation.

ARI. Lie still, complete bed rest they said. I was very obedient. Who knows what might have happened if I sat up or stood. By now, the almost constant pain in my head which subsided only for the short time the morphine did its job made me do as I was told. Any chaos or tension, relieved, momentarily while the drug stepped in to help. I remained flat on my back. I didn't want to risk a re-bleed by moving around too much, before safely getting through the surgery. The glare of the ward lights, even when my eyes were closed, was unbearable. It seemed like a bright torch being shone into my eyes. Blinds open, the view out of the window, the night sky, illuminated by the city lights. I longed for peace and quiet, soft lighting. The burning intensity of the lights and the noise, my mind was on edge. I grappled to decipher where the voices were coming from. What were they saying? Were the medical staff speaking to me? Usually no. Was it someone I knew, a visitor, a family member? Not yet. The din was excruciating, almost as hard to bear as the migraine effects of the brain haemorrhage itself. The voices continued. I decided they were for the patient in the bed next to mine. Was it common to be hypersensitive to sound after a brain bleed? I didn't know. Certain I didn't comment or complain, staff seemed to be alert to my anguish. They were quick to respond, rallying round to find me a private ward. Not having remained in the main ward long enough to even make eye contact with any other patients, I was transferred to my private room. It was my first night in ARI. No appreciation for the reasons why the other patients were there, I think I was introduced to Mr Currie, my neurosurgeon. At the time, to me, he was a male medic. Simply that, at that time. Nothing more…yet. I had no appreciation for his status or my requirement for his particular skills. At that time, I feel certain, that I would have heard him, but maybe felt too under the weather to actually listen. Digesting what he had to say, I probably left for my mum, dad and my sisters. In my own time, I would contemplate the words. I felt a mixture of excitement, relief and solace in my private room for one. Comforted by the calmness, I attempted to relax, while at the same time, hoped not to be forgotten about. Able to take deep breaths and relax, at least following shots of morphine being delivered to my hip, then arrived the bed pan. I'd never even heard of one before. Worried I would spill, the nurse assured me, no, all was safe. It's a genius invention, the bed pan. Fluids being pumped into me by the bagful, it was inevitable I would be calling for the bed pan at regular intervals. As it turned out, several times an hour. Better than having a catheter, although unknown to me, that would come, later. The nurse laughed. It wasn't long before she remarked that, from all the morphine jabs, my hip looked like a well-used dartboard.

I remember the time between my need for the morphine became less and less, as the drug itself took longer to take effect. I quickly seemed to become immune to the small dose. In order to feel its benefit, I pleaded for more of it and more often. Had I not been in hospital, I would have felt ashamed to be so desperate for a drug like morphine. But lying there and in pain, any thoughts of whether it was good, bad or whatever went out of my head as I frequently called for my much-needed narcotic. Coinciding with the relief I felt to be in the quiet private ward was the worry of at times being alone, particularly at night. I made sure that everyone around me was aware of my concerns. I was frightened that something sinister might happen, particularly during the night. A nurse or doctor wouldn't always be there.

I felt quite spoiled in my private room. Special treatment, why me? So well looked after, the drip in the back of my hand a new experience. Normally one to faint or feel faint when having a simple blood test, I was surprised at how well I coped with the variety and frequency of needles being plunged into my skin. I practised some distraction techniques when having the procedures. I certainly benefitted from being in bed.

I wasn't going to fall over from an already horizontal position while having blood taken. I felt my head had had enough to cope with, without reacting to the queasiness of blood tests. I concentrated hard on thinking about other things. Proud to overcome my fear of blood tests, subconsciously perhaps I knew that there was a bigger (surgery) mountain to climb, around the corner. I was satisfied that the blood tests were routine. They were going to happen many times during my stay. I therefore, manned up and got on with it.

Was I given much information before my operation? I don't remember. I thought, no. This made me trust that nothing too significant was going to happen. Then came the consent form for angiogram and one for surgery. Oh help. But, the forms seemed quite generic, didn't go into much detail. The hardest thing I thought I might have to deal with was a needle in the back of my hand, the GA. I'd had plenty of experience of needles and tests in the lead up to the surgery. I'd become used to that. At no time did I have a moment of clarity and realisation for what was actually going to happen.

Firstly, I needed to undergo a procedure that would determine the size and location of the burst aneurysm. The cerebral angiogram was performed by radiologist, Dr. Robb and involved anaesthetising my groin. A fine wire tube was inserted into the femoral artery of my right leg and fed up to my neck. A contrast solution of iodine was injected into the tube enabling the radiologist to view the condition of the blood vessels in the head. I could feel a warm liquid sensation as the iodine floated around my head. I kept my eyes closed. It felt like I was watching a cartoon of the road runner, only it was dark. He races off the cliff edge and plummets to the ground below, only to shatter into hundreds of pieces as though he was made of glass...breaking like a window as he hits the ground. My mind was playing crazy tricks on me. Fortunately by the time I experienced this sensation it coincided with the radiologist having completed the job of finding the offending, ruptured aneurysm. At the time I didn't know, but later found out, the iodine was a radioactive solution, what? I'd grown up around a nuclear power plant. I'd made it known to the family, when I was a child, that I wasn't comfortable living near a nuclear power plant. I didn't believe it was safe. I'd always intended to move away, for safety reasons when I grew up. I remember saying that I would live at least as far away as Inverness (Scotland). That felt safer to me, if there was ever a nuclear incident near our family home. I would already have a head start on getting away. Never querying the levels of iodine administered by Dr. Robb, I trusted the amount to be safe. At the time, my only knowledge was of the procedure and risk of stroke. I wasn't at the time, of sound enough mind as to enquire about the iodine. For determining location of the bleed, there wasn't an alternative procedure, so I accepted what was needed to be done. In future, if I am I ever to need iodine, I would certainly be having a new set of questions, before accepting that kind of medicine. No doubt I would be asking how much, how strong? Anyway, I came safely through the procedure and the location of the aneurysm was established. The iodine had successfully performed its duty. Lucky me! Free from any pain at the point of needle entry in my leg, a small bandage covered the evidence, preventing any blood seepage. With the angiogram procedure, more than one aneurysm is discovered in 30% of patients. Dr. Robb confirmed I just had the one. In no pain or discomfort from the procedure, only the unexpected crackling images in my head, I was returned to the ward. Some patients have a reaction to the procedure. There is an added risk of blood clot, stroke. Again, I am so lucky. Now wasn't the right time for me to query morbidity and mortality statistics. That came a little later. I later wondered if stroke risk during cerebral angiogram could be a result of plaque being dislodged somewhere on the wire's journey to the base of the brain. After my initial scary experience of the SAH, events seemed to work in my favour. Thankfully I avoided a rebleed. I am also so lucky to have escaped a stroke by clot as a result of the angiogram. I was fortunate to be deemed fit for surgery. Hopefully, being a non-smoking, fit and healthy vegetarian worked in my favour. I certainly wanted that operation, sooner rather than later. If the aneurysm was to rebleed before the operation, risk of dying would double, than after the initial bleed. While I didn't feel that the morphine was helping much as a painkiller, the psychological effect of the drug helped to prevent emotional outburst. That, I believe, helped to prevent a rebleed. I learned however, though, that there was a risk of dying during the operation. A patient's age, size of aneurysm and where it is located, are all factors associated with risk of death from a brain bleed. Being in the subarchnoid region, I believe, was in my favour, as was my age. The aneurysm bled into the subarachnoid space, an area on the surface of the brain. Did that mean that the aneurysm itself was in or close to the subarachnoid area? I hope so. The brain has such a complex web of structures, arteries and veins. The deeper within the brain the aneurysm, the more complex the surgery. Surgery might even be ruled out, if the aneurysm is considered to be inaccessible. Luck was on my side.

I was transferred to the high dependency ward immediately after surgery. I don't remember anything of that day after the anaesthetic going into the back of my hand. I don't think I was really aware of the enormity of the operation; the risks involved. Prior to the surgery, I had been a mix of frightened and calm. Frightened for potentially not waking up, calm knowing that I could return to lead a normal life afterwards. I think I kind of drifted along for a while after the operation. I guess I was coping with the aftereffects of the surgery – more headaches, the skull bones knitting together and such like. I wasn't aware of a bandage on my head, gave no consideration to how big it might have been. I couldn't see a tube poking out and draining excess fluid from inside my skull. Stitches hidden; I couldn't feel a catheter. No urge to need the bathroom. At 36 years old I couldn't believe how naive I was. This innocence served to protect me from fear, initially. Being woken every four hours for the medication I found quite exhausting. Following SAH, the drug nimodipine is administered every four hours for twenty-one days. A calcium-based channel blocker, the drug's aim is to prevent the risk of cerebral artery spasm i.e. blocking of blood flow to the brain.

I remember there were three of us in the high dependency ward. The other two, male I think, had been there longer than me. No idea their issues, I don't remember leaving my bed all the time I was in there. Mr Currie had warned me there would be a line coming from my neck. I had assumed he meant the anaesthetic had gone in through my neck. I didn't know the purpose of the line in my neck following the surgery, pain relief I guess and saline. There were three narrow tubes attached to the one needle in my neck. I was intrigued by it. It didn't make me feel sick. A bit of pressure on my neck where the needle was so it could be removed smoothly, and, just like that, it was out, 24 hours after the surgery. The discomfort lasting only for a moment, more due to the lack of familiarity. It was likewise with the catheter. I was surprised that I hadn't felt it at all while it was in. I was aware of it coming out. Thankfully, a quite straightforward procedure and over with within a few seconds. Surprised but relieved that my bladder was in normal working order, I hadn't appreciated I would have needed a catheter for the duration of the surgery and until I woke afterwards. Hadn't been on the priority list for topics of discussion. Thankfully it didn't require re-inserting.

I was reluctant, well scared to leave the safety of my bed. It had been vitally important before the surgery for me to remain horizontal at all times. That memory was still with me as I lay in the recovery ward. Head pounding like a migraine most of the time, I felt safer in bed. Get up and walk about, said the nurses, to aid my recovery. Still feeling weak after just a little over a week in bed, I chanced going as far as the bathroom and back to bed, in the hope that staff would be satisfied with my efforts. Funny how easily disorientated you can become. Being familiar with so many beds around the ward during the various stages of my stay, it was inevitable, as I attempted to navigate my way around for a bit of exercise, I would become lost.

The tube coming from a burr hole in my head must have been removed before I was fully awake. I remember Mr Currie saying it would be there to prevent bruising and swelling. By the time I woke up, it had gone. I was relieved to not witness that tube coming out. The tube enabled excess fluid to be drained away. The concertina apparatus would inhale and exhale as the fluid was expelled from my head, moved along the drain and gathered in the collection vessel. I was spared the details by my sisters until I was home, and my hospital stay was well in the past. My sisters' stomachs were weak, queezy at revisiting the details. I, on the other hand was intrigued to know as much as possible. It had been two weeks since I had thrown up. GA and brain surgery behind me, I was sick again. It was on the day of the surgery, after I had come round, or the day after, I'm not sure. I was still in the high dependency ward. Effects of the GA? A lack of food in my stomach for two weeks? Combination of meds on empty stomach? I wonder, do they not prescribe anti-sickness meds unless the patient complains? Good actually, to only get them if presenting with symptoms. I was on enough necessary drugs, without adding ones I might not need to take. I hadn't really eaten anything in over a week. My appetite gradually came back, a bit of toast here, some macaroni there. The first thing I ate after surgery was a small amount of soup. Maybe that had been the culprit that caused the vomiting. Weight loss concealed by bed clothes and spare blankets; I was back to struggling to keep warm.

Progress was announced. No longer in danger, I was transferred back to the general ward. It was good to acknowledge patients in the general ward this time. When I'd first arrived, the pain was too unbearable, the lights seemed too bright, the voices over-powering, all effects of the brain haemorrhage. In the general ward this time, I met Julie, not much older than me. Paralysed, Julie had suffered a stroke while hill climbing. I never did hear if she regained the use of her legs. Did she undergo surgery? I don't remember asking. Another neighbouring patient on the ward freely pointed out her catalogue of previous operations. I admired her for requesting tea and toast, immediately following back surgery. Wide awake, alert, I could have benefitted from a bit of her energy. Listless and in a trance-like state, I simply seemed to exist, taking in my surroundings, waiting for some adrenalin to kick in, until it was time to be discharged home. I wasn't ready to be open about my experience yet.

Head bandage off. My head felt lighter, like it does when you've had your hair permed and the rods are removed. What a sense of relief. All the tension vanished as the air got to my scalp, at last. The weight of the bandage gone, but the headache remained. I still had my long curly hair, my new perm only eight weeks old. I made tentative steps towards the bathroom. Hesitating before looking in the mirror, both sides of my head had been shaved. A black question mark shaped line pointed out the location of the surgery. I could arrange my remaining hair to hide the shaved patches. I took a moment to reflect on how my head looked – not my face, just my head. I decided that it wouldn't have mattered if all my hair was gone, bald. I was alive. So particular about the condition of my hair, much better to have short hair in good condition than long hair in bad. So grateful to be alive, my hairstyle was completely irrelevant, insignificant. For a moment, I considered I'd gotten off lightly. The poor patient next to me was resisting having a tube put down her throat. In through her mouth or nose, I'm not sure. It was so distressing to hear her complain. At the same time, thankful it didn't have to happen to me.

Ward 40 was such a special place. I never wanted to leave. I felt attached to the ward. It's time to set you free, uttered my surgeon Mr Currie. I didn't believe him, didn't want to. Did I feel ready? No, anyway, I couldn't go. My nieces and nephews were due to visit me on the ward at the weekend. You can stay until Thursday, agreed Mr Currie. Thankful for the additional night or two in hospital, the thought of being out, frightened me. Not ready to go it alone. Great news though, being declared well enough for discharge, absolutely. I'd become accustomed to the dependence. The thought of returning to the outside world, a bit overwhelming. Needed to find some way of coming to terms with it. My subconscious in overdrive, I knew I would have so many questions. If I stayed, I would have the opportunity to ask them all. The next day, Wednesday, college students; Sofie, Eilidh and Lachie arrived for a visit. Bearing gifts of Belgian Chocolates, my favourite, a great 'pick me up'. I would never fall asleep. Like chocolate, like candles, you can never have too many. By then, there was just the headaches and exhaustion to contend with. I struggled to stay awake for my visitors from the north. The next day after repeated threats from the nursing staff to get up, get dressed and get out, I eventually managed to motivate myself for departure. Discharge letter in hand, nurse Lorraine supplied me with a bucket load of painkillers to see me through the coming weeks; 100 paracetamol, morphine tablets and codeine I think, along with the nimodipine to be taken at 4 hourly intervals, until day 21 – 10th November.

Conscious decision to drink at least a litre and a half of water every day since coming out of hospital, my vice would have to be coffee. Seduced by the rich frothiness of a cappuccino, lured by the occasional, tempting hint of chocolate in mocha, oh man, but the calories. Forever grateful, my family had visited me every day in hospital, morning until night, mum, dad, and sisters Pauline and Maree. As well as to me, friends Anne, Wendy and Alison were a great support to my family. I don't know how we would have coped without them. Thoughts of my granny flickered in the back of my mind. On my last visit north to Caithness, to the nursing home where my granny was living, I had marked on her calendar that I would visit on Friday 21st October. Regular visits with granny were vitally important, especially while she was in care. Prior to living in the care home, granny enjoyed multiple daily visits from my mum and dad who lived next door to her. It turned out I had an unexpected appointment with the Aberdeen neurosurgery department on 21st October instead. I hated letting her down. Was she looking for me? No. My sister Pauline had called into her care home to let her know I couldn't visit. The details were kept from granny. The family thought granny was too frail to be given the news that I was sick. Granny was told I had a headache, and that the family were going south to be with me.

I didn't keep it to myself that I was worried to go to sleep especially when I was in the private ward. I feared my health might take a turn for the worse, during the night. These concerns, I shared with my family and ward staff. I didn't keep that to myself. I longed to be free of the shackles of my anxiety, determined not to bottle the issues up. I think I needed everyone to be aware, I was hyper alert to my situation. I was somehow prepared, should my health deteriorate further. It would come as less of a surprise. But, at the same time, I think the morphine induced a calmness that supressed any spontaneous outburst as a result of these worries. Anxiety decreased a little, but drugged, all the same, any motivation or burning desires subconsciously shelved. Not like me. But, I never once cried. Again, I think because of the drugs. Throughout life, granny lent a great ear. Her opinions were believable. I couldn't help but trust her advice. She gave great relationship advice. Granny saved me from self-pity on a number of occasions. This would have destroyed her, to see one of her family ill and for her words of wisdom unable to fix it. Had she survived to see me home and safe, no doubt she would have wanted to personally thank the staff of the NHS in Ward 40, especially Mr Currie, for their sterling efforts and unmistakably wonderful care in saving my life. Granny was a giver. She never was one who felt comfortable, taking. I guess she influenced me that way too, a little. Thank goodness for the morphine. It kept me calm, under control and ensured that my body didn't go into panic mode and risk setting off a chain of events. After such a shock, you can't risk a relapse carelessly.

Granny was my dearest friend. She thought I was brilliant, and I adored, admired and had a great respect for her. Little did I know that while my life hung in the balance, hers was nearing its end. My body switched instinctively into survival mode. I carefully had to place thoughts of granny into a compartment in my mind, protecting her memory. My brain, I think, didn't allow me to ponder about granny. It needed strength to get me through my hospital stay. For many years, granny had wrapped me in cotton wool with her love and affection; beds aired for days before I arrived to visit, electric blanket set to high AND a hot water bottle, the latter replaced with a newly poured hot bottle in the morning. Flash back to the late 70s/early 80s, my sister and I enjoyed cups of Tetley tea in bed and McVities digestives and butter served by granny, before breakfast. Stay in your beds, she would say to Pauline and me. That allowed granny to give full attention to preparing breakfasts for the guests in her B&B. She would then turn her undivided attention to my sister and me. This was during Easter and October holidays at her cosy house in John O'Groats. She had such strong morals and high principals. If I can be half the person granny was, I'll be satisfied. We were thoroughly spoiled, Pauline and me. One of the benefits of being the eldest two in the family.

Why am I plagued with the fear of recurring SAH? I don't know. I know I feel disrespectful of my surgeon who tells me I am safer. It's been treated, he said. Any one of us may have an aneurysm at any time. Mine has been treated. The arteries have been checked. They are clear. I want to trust. The feeling is at the forefront of my mind on a regular basis. I won't be surprised if it happens again. Of course, I hope it doesn't. No guarantee I would survive/recover next time. The GP who said I would get over it without the intervention of a neuro psychologist has no idea how it feels when such a fear is central to everyday activities. That kind of harsh manner is not at all helpful. Further to my concern that another brain aneurysm will develop is a fear for my family's safety. I worry that a brain aneurysm might occur in one of my sisters, nieces or nephews. They don't share my concerns. Their diet, fitness and lifestyles haven't changed as a result of this happening to me. With children to raise and nurture, my sisters prioritise them. The children take priority. There is no time to worry about their own health. They believe they are safe, and I admire them for their faith. Do I worry for my nieces and nephews? Yes! Crossing my fingers for them is what I do. They were so young when I had the SAH. They were warm and sincere, sharing their concern for me. I don't want to believe it will happen to one of them. It's just, the statistics are there. It's familial. Cousins, aunt, grand-parents, great grandparents, all affected. I hope my nieces and nephews are spared.

I need the flashbacks to losing consciousness. I want to fill in the missing pieces of the jigsaw puzzle. I keep expecting the fog to clear, my memory to close the gaps. I don't expect to suddenly cope with my fear as a result. I wonder, how was it before I passed out? Who witnessed it?

How was it when I came round and when I passed out again? Apparently I resisted an oxygen mask. Knowing that I struggled to breathe, strange I would resist oxygen. My neuropsychologist explained that forgetting is a protector. I won't recall any more details of my spontaneous brain bleed. I ask myself; will this make me stop trying to recall? I will aim to reduce the number of times I encourage the flashbacks. Perhaps there would be more trauma, if I were to remember all the details. Time to stop encouraging that memory.

My diagnosis was PTSD, a phobic disorder. I can justify feeling this way. I don't feel ashamed. I am not a hypochondriac. My specific fear included worry of a rebleed, that the metal clip in my head will dislodge, that a further aneurysm will grow and burst. This fear is in contrast to generalised anxiety or hypochondria which is fear in general. My surgeon Mr Currie, so experienced and approachable, pleasant mannered and knowledgeable. He is so highly skilled. I do trust his confidence that I am recovered. His clarity and reassurance for my safety seem diluted when he is no longer there. I do try and shake off my concerns. Why do the fears hover and haunt me like mirky grey ghosts? I wait for the thunder and lightning to strike in my head once more. I pray for a red sky at night. Being exposed to the unconsciousness, the feeling of near death, brought on the PTSD. The memory doesn't fade. It's vivid and lasting, as fresh as the initial occurrence. Betablockers are often prescribed to help with the condition. The trouble with betablockers though, while the physical pounding sensation of the heart subsides, the head is still consumed with anxiety. I believe the drugs can assist but cannot deal fully with the anxiety. I didn't take them. Instead, I relied on talking therapy.

I was twenty-one years old before I read my first novel; John Grisham's The Firm. Remarkably I had managed to scrape a 'C' pass in O'Grade English, having not studied for a single exam. More recently I have become hooked on anything by Douglas Kennedy, another American author. His main characters are young, successful, talented, high achievers who stumble into a web of crime. Since October 2005 I have become drawn to anything neurosurgical, in my quest to become informed of my condition. I pour over textbooks for hours feverishly, about the causes of brain aneurysms, whether they are hereditary, how many people are affected by aneurysms, what the survival rates are, what the surgery involves, the recovery time and return to work prognoses. I read and I re-read the same books. Do I think I might have missed something? Find something new on each revisit of the same old? Or, is it subconscious with the obsession of reinforcement?

It's Friday night, BBC2. I notice the party on television. Inquisitive for a moment, I listen to the programme, Aly Bain and his transatlantic friends on fiddles. Will I be tempted to watch? If I could, would I want to join in? Will I become hooked on the show? Curiosity over within a couple of minutes, I set the sound to mute. Periodically I glance at the screen while reading my latest purchase, 'Another Day in the Frontal Lobe'. I recognise the musicians; Aly Bain, Phil Cunningham, Bruce Molsky, Jenna Reid, Michael McGoldrick and Julie Fowlis. They are all players I have a great admiration for. I don't know why I don't care to hear the tunes. It's sad in a way to think that I don't want to be there on TV with them. At the same time, I witness their enjoyment as they share a smile and interact with one another in their joy. I keep waiting to feel I've made a mistake in leaving the music behind. I wonder, will I feel envious of these great players? I'm sure my friends are poised, waiting and expecting to hear me say, I've decided to play the fiddle again. Not yet!

NUDGED...

The Band

Was there a bond between us? Did the dancers in the group interact with the musicians? I remember we did. We always did. In equal measures, the quality of our performances was as vital to the band as it was to have fun. These were great times. Audiences witnessed the rapport between the band members. Our musical compatibility was enhanced when the band interacted with one another. It came naturally to us. With four core dance members in the group and three musicians, *Dannsa*, a professional dance company thrived on creativity. Taking traditional Scottish dance steps and intertwining them with contemporary choreography came naturally to dancers Caroline, Frank, Mats and Sandra. The musicians would collaborate with the dancers, with pipes, fiddle and song arranged to complement the dance choreography. The teamwork, I remember, was dream work. *Dannsa* commissioned the musicians of the band to compose new music for their new choreographies. How did it feel to be invited to create new music for the dancers? It was an incredible feeling. I remember, immediately setting about creating two pieces of music. One composition (Dannsa Hornpipe) was longer in length. The rhythm was dotted, and the notes intricate, it was more challenging to play. Frank McConnell's March, while less technically demanding, the phrasing of the tune was captivating. It would receive good feedback at concerts. Can you imagine how great it was to spend time with the band, with the dancers? Sounds like a fun journey, yes? I gave it up, why? These days, I ask myself the same question. What was it that prompted the change?

What was it like before the haemorrhage? How did it feel? If I go back to that summer, can I pinpoint a change? I look for clues that my health was deteriorating. I search for a sign that the volcano was about to erupt in my fragile head. In the summer of 2005, the band went out on tour. We travelled around Scotland. The tour finished in The Shetland Islands. With dancer, Mats hailing from Stockholm, two years previous we had toured Sweden. Caroline and Sandra were experienced in both Highland as well as modern dance. The athleticism of Highland dance required plenty of stamina. Both had it, in spades. To this day, Caroline and Sandra remain super fit and active. Just last autumn (2022), Sandra had me wild swimming in the river Spey. For me, not to be repeated, way too cold, I much prefer the North Sea. Toasty in comparison.

The free expression of the modern dance, combined with the discipline of Highland dance was unique to *Dannsa*. The dances, innovative, demonstrated the group's enviable flexibility and stamina alongside their artistic choreography. The boundaries of the individual disciplines were stretched as the core members of the group played with the many possibilities in combining the dance forms. Scottish step-dancing was another style explored by *Dannsa*. This involved beating out, percussive and rhythmic steps so common nowadays to the small island community of Cape Breton in Nova Scotia, Canada. Having virtually died out in Scotland, step-dancing was lovingly preserved and passed down through the generations in Canada by the fiercely patriotic descendants of the Scots. Individually, the members of *Dannsa* have visited Cape Breton to relearn the hard shoe, close to the floor dance style that resonates throughout the village halls around the stunning Island of Cape Breton that looks out to the Atlantic towards their homeland, Scotland. *Dannsa* initially mastered a core series of strathspey and reel steps. Originally a solo form of dance, Caroline, Frank and Sandra took the tradition and developed, choreographed routines set to the bagpipes, fiddle and Gaelic song. Working as a team, the three dancers honed their skills and embellished on original steps to create their own new dance patterns. At times, Caroline elevated with such elegance and beauty demonstrating a variation of a Highland dance while Sandra and Frank beat out a complementary synchronised step dance. The fusion of the two related dance forms resulted in an impressive display of their stamina and grace.

The other core member of the group was piper Fin Moore from Birnam, Perthshire. Fin's distinctive piping, gelled with the dancers, enhancing the impact the group had as an act. Fin's music was strong and percussive. It was so fitting and complementary to step-dancing. His knowledge of the tradition qualified him to suggest exactly the right tunes to support and complement *Dannsa's*, hard-shoe dancing. Fin's sensitivity to the tradition and style made him a vital member of the group. Fin was born to play for the Scottish/Cape Breton step-dance style.

Due to my term-time, work commitments at North Highland College, my role in *Dannsa* was itinerant fiddle player. This also enabled the dancers to have the flexibility to work with a variety of musicians. Traditional Scottish music and dance is often unique to the individual performing it. This allowed for *Dannsa's* performances constantly being refreshed as itinerant fiddle players and singers came and went.

Designated drivers for our 2005 Scottish tour included Frank, Caroline and Sandra. Each took it in turn to get us safely to our ports of call. Can you actually burn 150 calories by sitting playing fiddle? Surely not. Isn't that more calories than swimming? I decided to maintain a fitness regime by running each morning, while on tour. Envious of the dancers lean-ness and fitness, I punished myself each day by going for a run. I had to make an effort. I strided out on the pavements of the beautiful island of Bute (including a chilling swim in the sea there too, well more of a momentary dip), to the undulating single track road heading west of Gairloch, to the heather tapestry of purples and greens in Northwest Sutherland. I didn't really mind being a bit heavier than the dancers, so long as I was fit. Mid-August, we landed on the Shetland Isles. I began to feel quite exhausted. I struggled to run downhill. By now, only able to walk uphill, dancer friend Sandra very graciously kept me company. No sign of Caroline. She would sprint off into the distance, unaware of the lethargic me, almost crawling behind. Sandra could have so easily vanished at speed with Caroline. Instead, no, she kept me company. Was that a sign that the aneurysm had begun to grow? Who knows. There is no knowing how long an aneurysm grows for before bursting. Specialists debate as to whether they grow within a few hours, a few days or weeks before bursting. I certainly felt the benefit of stopping running after the Shetland leg of our tour. It enabled me to try and recharge my batteries.

It wasn't a knee-jerk reaction, going to the doctor about my huge dip in energy. The coldness I felt, especially for the time of year, quite unusual for me. I was referred to a nurse. On attending the appointment, I realised she was a psychiatric nurse. I was puzzled. Anyway, do you care about your appearance? was the nurse's first question. More than a little offended, in fact, it prompted me to notice, and wonder the same about her. Her ankle length, peach, floaty skirt and red, knitted jersey combo were never going to match. Okay, maybe I was a little young for the long, brown, knitted cardigan with Fair Isle design, a hand-knit I had inherited from my grandma. It was of sentimental value to me, not an indication of a mental health condition. The nurse's face, like the blade of an axe, her insults had affected me. At least the colours of what I was wearing, were co-ordinated with one another. I'd simply been struggling to shake off the shivers and tiredness. I wouldn't have said I was a shoddy dresser. My energy levels had been dropping, steadily that summer. Admittedly, you would never catch me in a power suit. In any case, I had no need to be wearing that sort of attire. I suppose I was feeling a little down, the effects of feeling cold and tired. Probably, nothing that a few iron tablets couldn't sort out, if she had considered asking what I thought. Maybe I had abandoned my routine that day, going make-up free, to the medical appointment. Her next question, did I have suicidal thoughts? Not at all!

I feel very fortunate to have joined *Dannsa* on many exciting musical trips. Our week-long tour of Sweden in the summer of 2003 was a stand-out. We travelled with Ryanair from Prestwick to the outskirts of Stockholm. We shared a few gins and tonics on the flight. For me, the tour felt like a holiday. I say holiday because as musicians and dancers we are so fortunate to do something we love for a living. At times, it didn't feel like work. The added benefit with *Dannsa* was that first and foremost we were all very good friends. Second to that we were lucky to be compatible musically. While the girls went running each morning, the boys took advantage of the opportunity to sleep on. Always the comedian, one day Frank inquired about what speed we were running at. I promptly demonstrated, setting off barefoot along the water's edge. Unaware at the time, Frank did his best to walk, briskly behind me. He managed to keep up, saying, 'call that running?' Ok, my interpretation of running equalling Frank's walk was quite laughable. Call it, gentle jog. I'll put it down to my background in Highland Dance, where the focus is more on elevation than travelling a great distance. It was exercise, and that was the point. The summer sunshine in Sweden enabled us to rehearse outdoors. The serene, stillness of the canals made practising by them quite therapeutic. We were afforded the luxury of some Swedish Volvo Estate cars for our trip. They came complete with cruise control. Spoiled, the Swedish hostel was also pretty fancy. Not at all a rustic, basic, like you would associate with hostel accommodation at home.

Precious? What was that? Well, when not in reference to a niece or nephew, I would be talking about my fiddle. A year, it took, to pay my dad back for four-figure sum I borrowed to buy the fiddle. Alasdair and a whole load of other fiddlers said I needed a better one. Better do as I was told. I went shopping with Alasdair (Fraser), Ifshin Violins, near where Alasdair lived, California. What better endorsement than to have Alasdair Fraser's approval?

Back to *Dannsa* for a bit. I would seize any opportunity to play fiddle along with piper, Fin. An old head on young shoulders, there was such maturity in his playing. In terms of musicianship, Fin was grounded in the tradition. He had enormous respect for the old style of playing. Fin's dance style and use of rhythm were hypnotic. Every note was afforded the utmost of attention that sent listeners into a zone. Audiences would naturally focus on Fin's every note, his every embellishment of every note and the ease at which he appeared when playing the most challenging of Scottish tunes. I was hooked on Fin's playing. When I reflect on what it was like to play along with Fin, he on pipes and me on fiddle, it was a partnership, an effortless connection of two very individual musicians who fed off one another, inspiring each other all the time to play on the offbeat, take the lead or throw in a variation, a low octave melody or a rhythmic harmony. That unspoken communication was a very valuable and special thing. It really is a rare and magical experience when you find a musician like Fin. I am forever grateful for that musical partnership. It's when the music isn't too fast, and it isn't too slow. The nuances occur spontaneously, and each player subconsciously responds to it.

Determined, passionate about the music, why had I given in to radical change? As I write I wonder, why on earth did I want to pack it in? In Sweden our performances began with Fin playing a set on the big, the loud, the Highland Pipes. Louder than a pneumatic drill, the Highland bagpipes can reach 111 decibels when played outdoors. Not everyone's cup of tea, I have vivid memories of still hearing the sound of the pipes for days after a Highland dancing competition. Unavoidable, the ringing was stubborn. All the time, the repertoire of tunes was expanding in my head, no effort needed. This opening number in Sweden, commanded the attention of everyone within a two-mile radius of our platform. Then the dancers would join in; Caroline and Sandra adorned in white linen dresses, bought by Caroline at an Italian market and modified to reflect our Scottishness with the addition of tartan trim; Buchanan tartan if I remember rightly. The focus of attention immediately went to the dancers as they moved in a figure of eight, before setting to one another. The percussive beats, taps and brushes on the wooden platform were mesmerizing and audiences would be captivated at the foreign displays of synchronisation and precision being portrayed before them.

Am I sad when I recall these special musical times? No, I don't think so. I try to maintain a positive outlook. I didn't want to have the feeling of missing the music. No mourning allowed. I had happy memories of great times. I couldn't wait to plug the gap left by my music. In the intervening years, I read, travelled a bit, worked and spent time with family and friends. I enjoyed not playing music. I didn't miss the practising, performing or teaching. I valued time with friends, musician friends and non-musician friends. Not being judged, for not playing music anymore, I really appreciated. My choosing to stop playing fiddle was irrelevant to the true friends. Was it a choice, though? Giving up the fiddle? Deep down in my heart, I felt I had no choice but to park the music. I was shocked. It was so unexpected. I struggled a bit with the guilt I felt. It was as though I was letting people down. To an extent, I felt there was an expectation I would return to my music, after recovery. The letting go of such an important and significant gift made a fundamental change to my life. What would I do? What would come after fiddle for me? I couldn't simply switch from being good at something, to being instantly good at something else. I would need to practice something else. Would I have the drive to replace fiddle with some other skill? I didn't know. Firstly, there was the determination to abandon the fiddle. I had faith that something to replace fiddle in my life would come along. Could I find something of equal value to take its place? I didn't know. But I was keen to find out. There are so many gifted musicians. Happy to let the opportunities I had enjoyed go, I waited, to see what I might end up doing in place of music. No time to feel guilt. A bit of selfish makes a survivor.

At times, previously, I felt like I had first refusal. For example, when it came to teaching at Sabhal Mòr Ostaig, alongside Alasdair Fraser. Although, I don't remember a specific conversation, we just did it. I was comfortable when the door opened for another musician to take my place. Good for them! I trusted that something else would come along for me. I had been lucky, many times, to win funding to attend courses in California, Limerick and South Uist. I made the most of those opportunities, absorbed like a sponge on the one hand and shared my newly learned techniques freely on the other. That's the way it needs to be. As a learner you need to be focused and alert to the gems that emanate from good teachers. As a good teacher, I believe it's your whole sense of purpose to find ways to deliver that magic in a way that players of all abilities can benefit. So important, the message, never to feel threatened. The learner might supersede the teacher in terms of ability. It's vital to be confident in your own personal playing ability and quality, without fearing that the next person is better. Supportive and appreciative environments are key in music.

People were disappointed when I stopped playing and teaching fiddle. In time I got over the guilt, well most of it! Although quite an inhibited person in general, I put as much consideration and deep thought into decision making as a person who is freely able to express themselves. A part of me thinks I should have continued as a musician. If I had, I would be doing it for all the people who said I was making a mistake. That is a consideration. A bigger part of me got selfish. The thrill and anticipation of discovering a new direction in life appealed to me. I didn't think that on one occasion. I felt it every day for many months. For months the thought consumed me as much as thinking about the brain haemorrhage was at the forefront of my mind almost every moment of the day.

As I recuperated from surgery at my sister Pauline's house on weeknights, I would stay with my mum and dad on weekends. The fiddle sat in the corner of their living room, tucked away in its box, ignored. Visitors would comment on seeing it. Enquiries were made about when the fiddle would next come out and be played. Deep down I was harbouring thoughts, serious considerations of not wanting to be a musician anymore. I would tell myself, don't make a hasty decision. I wanted to take my time, decide when the time felt right. I couldn't rush the decision. But how soon was long enough? How would I know if I had waited long enough to decide on giving up my music? At the time I didn't realise it. On reflection, I feel quite certain that whatever career I had been doing before the SAH, I would have had to change. It wasn't so much about not enjoying playing music anymore. It wasn't about not wanting to teach the music I'd grown up with; the music my parents had enthusiastically encouraged me to embrace and pursue; the music I had subsequently relayed to others who were as crazy about the tradition as

I had been. It was about my reaction to a huge shock. Other things became a priority for me. Yes, I felt guilt when neighbours, friends and family said they wanted me to play the fiddle. The selfish side of me took over. I decided that I needed to do what was right for me at the time. Would turning my back on the fiddle just be for the short term? I didn't know. Might it be a long-term change? Others said to me, they missed not hearing me play. People wished I would play again. In the beginning I think I was quite dismissive about the comments. I didn't fully appreciate the joy others got from hearing me play. Ultimately, I told myself it wasn't about what other people wanted. Initially I had the valid excuse of extreme exhaustion. Off the hook for a bit, I struggled to justify my rejection of the fiddle to people, after a few short months.

I have attempted here to justify my turmoil around the music. In reading my book, I hope you can understand. From my point of view, giving up my music was a big decision to make. I truly respected that so many people cared about me, about my music. I feel so fortunate to have maintained such important friendships with musicians who didn't criticise me for not playing anymore. I am lucky to have great friends and family.

Can you imagine, being told, that you are no longer attractive to someone, because you have given up the fiddle? No overnight decision, I agonised for several months before giving up my music career. Those shallow comments cut deep at the time. I've endured worse. It wasn't the first time I'd had to pick myself up and dust myself off. I don't believe that was the real reason for the dumping. If only he'd had the courage to be honest. Did I feel like I was disrespecting other musicians, when I gave up playing? To an extent, I think I did. Having enjoyed many opportunities over the years, had I taken them from a fiddler who could have appreciated and developed their career, as a result? I don't know. What I do know is, that it wasn't pre-meditated. I hadn't wanted to withdraw from music. I felt the illness had drawn me away from the music. Thank goodness for true friends who accepted my giving up the music. It was so liberating to have the support of great friends and family. I was confident enough in my ability as a musician not to feel that I was no great loss to the fiddle world. I did appreciate that some people may have felt I was careless in discarding my musical talent. At the same time, I'm sure these people understand that the catalyst for the change was in fact having endured the SAH. I hope I was eventually forgiven. I feel that the door was opened for others to take advantage of the playing and teaching opportunities I had once enjoyed.

To all of you who felt let down by my packing the music in, I hadn't lost the ability to play. I continued to love the company of musicians. When requested to play or join in with fiddlers, I didn't mind. You can probably sense my reticence. I truly didn't mind playing if asked to. A part of me was sad when I didn't feel the music in the way I used to. I didn't revel in the music. My heart wasn't in it for a long time. At the time, I was so thankful to have my mobility so that I was able to play and do other dextrous things. Many people who have suffered a brain injury have long term mobility problems, speech and/or neurological deficit. It was five months after surgery before I picked up my fiddle to play it. I was anxious to know whether I would be able to play like I used to. In my mind I felt that I could. It wasn't until my fingers made contact with the strings on the fingerboard and I began to move them, I realised nothing had changed. On so many levels I have been so extremely lucky, both before and since the SAH. I haven't mentioned until now: I have sold my fiddle! Okay, slightly out of date this paragraph. Imagine you are reading this and it's the year, 2006.

I feel that I had to endure a number of adverse comments to my suggesting I was giving up the fiddle long before the final day came, and I sold my precious Maggini (fiddle). In some ways, dealing with that life changing decision was as painful to endure as the haemorrhage and immediate aftermath itself...with thoughts of both events forever in my mind, although I am glad to say that thoughts of the fiddle were in the back of my mind, only coming to the forefront when a friend or relative made comment on the subject. Whereas thoughts of the SAH would be constantly at the forefront of my mind in the early years. I never gave a single thought to my fiddle all the time I was in hospital. Visitors, friends or family didn't mention fiddle either, I recall. Why might that be? Probably, deliberately, to save from upsetting me. Music can mean the world to people, players and listeners alike. I'm sure they were sensitive initially to the thought that I may have had difficulty in remembering how to play, as a result of my brain injury. As soon as I was discharged from hospital the fiddle seemed to be the main topic of conversation amongst my family and friends, of course in addition to my head and recovery.

My music was my life. It was my whole life. Nothing else in my life was more important to me than my family, my granny, my fiddle and granny's cat. I never imagined that I would be sitting here right now, writing this book and not be a musician anymore. I don't remember exactly when I began to feel a change coming on. It was some time on or after the 4th of November 2005, the day I was discharged from Ward 40. I used to believe that a life without music was simply unimaginable. I suppose in some ways I do still believe in its magical qualities. There is therapy in music, in listening to it. Ironically, the very thing that had been my medicine in life, my staple diet, I gave up, cast aside and neglected. I decided I no longer needed the music in the shape it had been in my life. It became unwanted, like a badly fitting pair of shoes. I felt such relief and freedom to flex my stifled toes when I flung off my ill-fitting footwear.

NUDGED...

Fiddle Story

I had been undeterred in my quest to become a good fiddle player. As a teenager, I spent countless hours practising daily. Unsatisfied playing the bare bones of the written melody, I longed to embellish the tunes with colour and texture. Inspired by 20th century great fiddlers, I would listen, learn and play along to vinyl recordings and VHS tapes. Playing not yet matured, I strived to incorporate complexity and skill. I utilised dynamics, built in variation, weaving my own originality around the framework of tunes. I was getting there. Eager to devour the old Highland Fiddle repertoires, I immersed myself in; The Atholl, Skye and Patrick MacDonald collections. I thrived on the challenge to be able to sight read with ease. Slowly, carefully, tiptoeing amongst the strathspeys and reels of my upbringing, I learned to interlock, segment by segment of the music, until I had complete melodies in my grasp. Aly Bain, master fiddler from The Shetland Isles was exhilarating to listen to. His flamboyant approach was captivating. The phrasing of the music so easily demonstrated, the tension and relief in the phrasing of the tunes, Aly excelled in, his personality revealed through the fiddle. Aly played at lightening pace and with precision, he still does. He somehow managed to inject dazzling rhythm, unpredictable swing and syncopation, powerful energy and a commanding passion as he weaved around intricate melodies. Whether performing high energy lyrical reels or an emotive slow air, Aly captured the magic of the tune with ease. He had, still has a way of depicting the mood with the finesse and grace usually associated with classical players. A fire of musical passion was ignited, every time I listened to Aly Bain launch into old Shetland melodies or his own self-penned compositions. Have you heard him play? You might have, but not realised. Aly made a programme once for television with former BBC Young Musician of the Year, violinist, Nicola Benedetti. In the programme, Aly performs flawlessly with ease, alongside classical violinist Nicola. The purity and cleanness of Aly's fiddle playing combined so beautifully with Nicola's: the difference in styles working in harmony with one another.

When did I start learning fiddle? I was about ten or eleven years old I think when I first decided that I wanted to learn. A lack of tuition in our rural, Highland hamlet meant I had to wait a little longer. My sisters, brother and I grew up in a fiercely patriotic household. Dad was self-taught on the accordion. Every night we were exposed to Scottish dance music on his Honor box. I was impressed and mesmerised at dad playing any tune by ear. He was inspired by the late Jimmy Shand initially and later by accordionists Seumas O'Sullivan, Gordon Pattullo and the late Paddy Neary to name a few. A good sense of timing and rhythm are vital to being a good, dance musician. Being a Highland dancer as well as listening to my dad playing tunes on the accordion instilled in me, good timing and good rhythm. Mum a keen dancer, meant there was no shortage of traditional music and Highland culture at home, when it came to inspiration. To this day, I value the fact our family were immersed in and had respect for our culture and traditions. Subconsciously, Scottish music was washing over me all the time I was growing up. I do believe it was a case of transferring what was in my head to whatever instrument I ended up deciding to learn. The repertoire was there already. I just needed to decide on the instrument, and to put in the hours of practice.

Determined to grasp a bit of Aly Bain's magic, I eventually got started on my own musical journey. I must have been around 17 years old, when I was able to tackle learning some of Aly Bain's tunes from his recordings. I avidly absorbed Aly's repertoire from his LPs Lonely Bird and Aly Bain, the tunes that were within my technical capability that is. My keen ear sparked a new challenge for me. I resolved to memorize Aly's entire albums. Persistent, motivation increased, I set about the task. I have to say however, that I preferred to play at a slightly more sedate pace, a slightly less frenetic tempo. Ok, I actually couldn't keep up with him, had I wanted to. Seriously though, in order to play for dancing which I loved to do, demanded a more rhythmic approach to playing, achieved by playing a little slower.

The Down-Home series on television in the 1980s featured the impressive Aly Bain. I remember passing many hours at a family friend's house on the Orkney Islands. I would play back the video tapes and practice along to the sets of tunes that gave an insight into Aly's fiddling. This also exposed me to the fiddle music of North America, in particular the small island community of Cape Breton, Nova Scotia. In the years that followed, as I endeavoured to become an accomplished musician, the fiddle music of Cape Breton Island would hold me firmly in its grip in a way that no other style has impressed on my playing. Many of the people who live on Cape Breton Island are descendants of the Scots. Thousands of Scots emigrated to Canada, in the late 1700s and early 1800s. In Scotland, wealthy landlords cleared the native Highlanders from their land to make way for the more profitable business in sheep farming. Families were uprooted from their pockets of arable croft holdings and ousted, cleared to hostile, peripheral land where they struggled to eke out a meagre existence in pursuit of survival. With the aim and hope of discovering a better life, ultimately many Highlanders emigrated to North America, taking with them their customs and traditions. Many of the emigrants settled on Cape Breton Island and assigned place names to their new territory which would remind them of home, the old country, Scotland. If you travel to Cape Breton Island today you will pass through Glendale, Glencoe, Inverness and Dingwall, all reminders of familiar places in Scotland. You will meet Mackays, MacMasters, MacNeils, MacIsaacs and MacDonalds. Everywhere you go on the island you are faced with reminders of the ancestry of the people there.

1986 saw the twinning of the Highlands of Scotland with Cape Breton Island, Nova Scotia. As a member of Caithness Junior Fiddlers, I was lucky enough to embark on a three-week tour of Cape Breton with the group. My place was secured due to one group member having to withdraw. The opportunity could have so easily slipped through my fingers. I had been on the reserve list. At this stage, my ability to play fiddle was extremely limited. Not fully feeling that my place on the trip was deserved, it didn't hinder my enthusiasm for going. Witnessing musicians in Canada perform from memory (without sheet music), was new for us. It was intriguing. When I reminisce of the trip, I distinctly remember meeting the Cape Breton family band The Barra MacNeils. At the time, they were an up-and-coming band of traditional musicians. Today they are at the leading edge of folk music in Canada and have continued to build on their success of the 1980s. Lead fiddle player in the band, Kyle MacNeil has a unique ability to fuse the artfulness of classical music with his native Cape Breton, musical dialect. The result is that he is in command of the most challenging tunes in terms of key and range while at the same time inspiring audiences to dance a rhythmic Highland reel or jig. The Barra MacNeils playing ability stood out. I have vivid memories of the complexity of their playing. In many ways, it reminds me of the Northeast style in Scotland, polished, grand. It was enthralling to watch, as fascinating as watching Aly Bain.

My visit to Cape Breton in 1986 was a turning point for me. I wanted to construct and demonstrate eloquent phrasing. I wanted my music to be riveting and engaging to listen to. I wanted it to be complex and at the same time free. I saw it as critical that music should reach out to the audience and bring out the best in a player. I aspired to learn the Caithness Junior Fiddlers repertoire by ear (off by heart) upon my return from Canada. I yearned to up my standard of playing. This was a good place to begin. I was 16. I gradually built up a repertoire of about twenty sets of tunes. The music demanded a new goal for me to pursue. In traditional Scottish music there is scope for complete freedom to interpret a tune in any style. Unlike classical music which comes complete with the composer's intentions in terms of interpretation: traditional music often only comes with the notes and no suggestion for interpretation. To the traditional player this is expected. I needed to know how to read the tune, to make it my own. I understood dynamics. I had to know how and when to incorporate them. I studied Aly Bain's playing closely, and later Alasdair Fraser, a Scot living in California, Jerry Holland and Buddy MacMaster of Cape Breton and Mairead Ni Mhaonaigh from Donegal in the Northwest of Ireland. These hugely inspirational musicians and teachers taught me how to bring my music to life. Having received scholarships to attend The Valley of the Moon Scottish Fiddle School in California, on no less than four occasions, I travelled to America to study under Alasdair, Buddy and Mairead. Tuition was outdoors in the woods, two hundred enthusiastic American fiddlers and me, hungry to get some rhythm into our reels, some syncopation into our strathspeys and some dirt into our dance tunes. The dirt is what makes the music authentic. Many of us had been taught to play clean, to portray exactly what was written on the page. In these workshops, the teachers focused the energy on finding what wasn't on the page. They demanded that the class decide just how much meat should be on the bones of the tune. In traditional music the challenge is that the tune constantly evolves. Each time you play the tune you should delve into your bag of technique tricks and bring out something new. This way the listener continues to be entertained, the tune is unpredictable and therefore it stays alive. Specks of light sparkle and dance on the blank canvas of melody. The tunes become enriched by an abundance of textures; the musician imprints his/her artistic creativity on the piece. The artist at work fills the landscape, keeps the performance unpredictable. Like a painting, there is random light and shadow, unexpected phrase patterns, delicate branches embellish the skeleton of the tune. The tune comes alive with a full body of rich variations.

I would spend hours listening to and watching Buddy MacMaster. Sitting right in front of Buddy, at summer schools on the Isle of Skye, I could see exactly how much bow he used, what part of the bow he used, where he made contact between the bow and the strings and how much pressure he applied. I strived to mimic Buddy in my attempts to create his sound, but only as a road to finding my own musical voice. I experimented in the same way with Mairead's style. Similar to Buddy's in many ways, Mairead's style was quite animated. Both players had a single bow style i.e., up, down, up, down. However, I remember that Mairead's bow maintained contact with the string for longer, creating an elongated continuous, solid sound, while Buddy's variation of lifts and legato was more of a challenge to achieve. The lifts were never in the same place each time the tune was played. Buddy constantly varied his approach to the bowing, maintaining that challenge to emulate him. Patient and committed, I had a self-belief when it came to fiddle, eventually.

A trained teacher, Mairead was very articulate. Her teaching was fun, the tasks attainable. I realise how fortunate I have been to attend the course in California, in the summers of 1988, 1990, 1994 and 2000. In addition to The Valley of The Moon Fiddle School, I attended the University of Limerick Blas Summer School twice. A two-week, intensive course in style, repertoire and history of Irish Music and Dance, the courses were directed by, the now late, Michael O' Suillibhean. Classes were led by a team of experienced instructors, unfazed by mixed ability groups. Classes comprised complete beginners all the way through to advanced players, together. The tremendous Martin Hayes commented on my style. I didn't give enough attention to the off-beat notes, he said. The result was an over-syncopation. I could appreciate his feedback and learned a lot from taking his opinion on board. At the time I remember thinking it was worth going to Ireland just to hear that one piece of advice. Another highlight of that journey for me was meeting Irish dancer Colin Dunne of Riverdance fame. I was enchanted by his percussive and rhythmic step dancing which was completely improvised on one occasion when he accompanied the course teachers: Niall Keegan and Brian Finnegan on Flutes, Sandra Joyce on Bodhran and Michael O' Suillibhean on piano. That was such a rare treat and something I will remember forever.

I was a good fiddle player. I was a better fiddle teacher. Sight read or play by ear (off by heart), I later found it easy to do both. You are a more versatile player and therefore at an advantage over a musician who can only do one or the other. I recognise I had my limitations, however. But, when faced with a class, you focus on what you CAN do, not on what you can't. Your aim is to enrich the teaching and learning experience. Your goal is to inspire, to enthuse, to encourage, to support, to challenge and most of all to have fun.

Reading sheet music is like reading a book. You always look ahead. You let your short-term memory absorb the meaning. You anticipate what will come next. As with songs where you can usually predict the rhyming phrase, a sound knowledge of traditional Scottish music means you know where the tune is going next. A good player can anticipate where a phrase of music demands particular attention...short bow strokes, long bow strokes, neat articulation and varied dynamics It is vital to place the focus in a different place in the tune the next time around. It takes a special skill to interpret a tune at speed. Intuition based on past experience enables a good player to translate the skeleton of the tune into a meaningful landscape.

At the forefront of my mind had always been the importance to undertake personal and professional development. Not satisfied with annually, I would seek out opportunities on a regular basis. We can always learn more and I strongly believed that it was important for me to continue to attend courses, not only to make me a better and more versatile player, but to also make me a better teacher. Attending a psychology for musicians' course, London, 2004 was one of the highpoints in my professional development quest. The only traditional musician amongst twenty-five classical players, I was quite overwhelmed. It was easy to feel like a fish out of water. As some participants had taken the course the previous year, I was instantly impressed. What better endorsement than to have returning students. I sensed it was going to be a great week. It did not disappoint! The annual, week-long course, highly practical in nature, centred on a range of issues such as performance anxiety, rhythm, timing, parent/pupil/teacher conflict, dance and innovative teaching methods. Some of the approaches to and content of the teaching were quite unorthodox. I was intrigued and excited. This course really turned by approach to teaching, on its head. With a course of my own to teach, just around the corner, I was energised to get utilising my newfound, London approach to teaching fiddle. An intensive week, experimenting with new teaching methods, intrigued and inspired me. I became fixated on the benefits of the course. I had a thirst to soak up the advice and pass it on. I immediately went to Sabhal Mòr Ostaig Gaelic College on the Isle of Skye the following week and incorporated these new ideas into my teaching. With around thirty fiddlers to a class, I was slightly apprehensive about whether the group would buy in to my new London approach to teaching. The result was astounding. The groups were very obedient, tried everything I threw at them and appreciated and benefitted from these ways, buying into it without resistance. Psychology in my university degree had taught me, the sooner and more often that learning is reinforced and practiced, the more embedded the learning will be. Having a course to teach the very next week after my London course reinforced the learning. With all the newly learned techniques fresh in my mind plus large class to deliver the new approach to, I was off to a head start. The goal was to aim for active participation in classes. I was less mentally drained at the end of the teaching day. Students retained what they had learned for longer. By asking open questions of the class, fiddlers were prompted to think. The learners were responsible for resolving some of their own barriers to fiddling. I strongly recommend any music teacher to attend the Psychology for Musicians course. For anyone with no formal training in teaching, that course is a must. Passing the effort of learning onto the student, enables a more thorough and longer-lasting result. Students more engaged, teacher, less drained.

As with the band Dannsa, it is when I recall these special and memorable times that I question why I felt the need to give it up. For many years, I didn't feel differently about my decision. I could understand why others thought it strange when I stopped playing and teaching fiddle. In some ways it was like when a relationship comes to an end. We often remember only the good times. That can make us question whether the relationship should have ended. Anyway, with the decision made, it's important to pick oneself up and go in search of new special memories to create. The more I thought about giving up my music career, the more excited I became. I couldn't wait to find other challenges to fill my time. Being a good music teacher and performer didn't come instantly to me. I spent years really struggling to learn. I think that made me a better teacher. Being a fiddler who had grappled with the complexities of learning to play fiddle, I had first-hand experience of the difficulty. To a large extent I had to overcome those challenges alone. I felt I could really appreciate what it was like to learn and achieve. I would set my fiddle goals and finding ways of reaching them. I went to as many workshops, summer schools and classes as I could find to better myself, seeking out the people who in my opinion were the best teachers and players. There came a point where a musician didn't have to be a great teacher for me to learn a lot from them. My experience over the years meant that I would find the styles and techniques in their playing without it being spelt out to me segment by segment. I was excited to be able to learn that way but, like I said, it was no walk in the park. I had really struggled from the age of thirteen when I first picked up the fiddle until I was about twenty.

After I had physically (I think) recovered from the trauma of the SAH, I went back to my day job at the college. I fulfilled a few freelance engagements that had been arranged prior to the brain injury. I believed in the North Atlantic Fiddle Convention, organised by The Elphinstone Institute at the University of Aberdeen. Not wanting to let the festival down, I practised like crazy for five weeks. I wasn't a naturally gifted performer. I enjoyed the challenge of setting standards and preparing a programme of music that would hopefully entertain. I was proud of what we had achieved for the festival. My long-time friend Pete MacCallum accompanied me. It was a five day event. I sent him my set list on cd, to work out some chord arrangements on guitar. I enjoyed the moments of exposure. It was rewarding. I, we got a lot out of doing it. The North

Atlantic Fiddle Convention was a great week. In hindsight, it was how I would imagine a holiday romance. Deep down I knew the fiddle would go back in its case at the end of the week. I sometimes wonder where my drive, my passion and craving to play and teach had gone. My longing to improve as a performer, a teacher, where did it go? I even went so far as to donating my entire library of music books to the local college. Quite minimalist anyway, I wouldn't be needing sheet music, if I was no longer playing fiddle. Until 2017, I think, I didn't get so curious as to keep trying to get really good just in case I might enjoy it again. Anyway, I sold my Italian fiddle, my English case and German bow, 2006, I think? Big mistake? At the time, I thought, definitely, no!

I think my proudest moment on stage was July 2006. Performing with Pete on guitar was always a treat, The Lemon Tree Arts Centre in Aberdeen on that occasion. I have very special memories of Aberdeen. My life was saved there. I did my undergraduate masters degree in Gaelic Studies there from 1994-1998. To perform there to a full-house was a career highpoint. There's been so many of them. At the same time, it served as the beginning of the end of my music career. First though, when I compared receiving such magnificent treatment in Ward 40, I had to give something back. Yes, we have the NHS and we pay our National Insurance contributions and taxes. I just didn't feel comfortable taking that immense gift of life saving treatment and care without doing my bit to repay the NHS. I did it, in the way I know how, by making a CD recording. The money raised through CD sales of my album, Ward 40, was given to the Staff Fund, Staff Training Fund and the general fund for resources - all for Ward 40 neurosurgery, ARI. I see my contribution as barely scratching the surface of the needs of the ward. It was a thought I had one day, and within a few short weeks, became a reality. I was excited to raise around £10,000 for the ward. It's a subjective feeling. Something I know how to do. A part of me has the confidence, I lean on those who can help. Maybe I should have switched to working a day job in sales rather than purchasing.

My Tune

In the summer of 2004 I secured a fiddle teaching job alongside fellow Scot, Alasdair Fraser. This was a huge achievement. So many great fiddle players in Scotland, yet he picked me. How excited was I to be chosen? Very! The annual, week-long course had been established in 1987. The opening year had 25 participants. I was one of them. The venue was University of the Highlands & Islands, Sabhal Mòr Ostaig campus on the beautiful Isle of Skye. Every year since the course inception, musicians came in their throngs. Alasdair an inspirational musician and teacher, lived in California. You had to grab your chance to absorb his magic. Couldn't risk waiting another whole year before Alasdair returned to his native Scotland to perform and teach again. From 1987 to 1993 I myself attended the course as a student of Alasdair's. An enthusiastic fiddler with potential, I was eager to soak up Alasdair's message. Like a sponge, I listened, copied, listened again, copied some more and practised hard. My quest? At the time, I longed to be a great fiddle player. Never in my wildest dreams did I think I would improve so much as to want to or be able to teach. It was some years before I gained enough confidence to pass on my own learnings to others. Alasdair's enviable command of the instrument coupled with a unique skill to pass on his knowledge and inspire, reached out to players of all ages and abilities. As the years went by, the numbers attending Alasdair's, Skye Summer School, expanded. Word got round. Alasdair had been playing concert tours, before and after teaching at the Skye summer school. Audiences were hooked. He dazzled with his knowledge of Scottish music history. The web of fascinating stories that Alasdair weaved into his performances, brought his shows to another level. To this day, they still do. Alasdair would talk about the famous Gow family of fiddlers and composers. At times you would think Alasdair had been a fly on the wall, a witness, at meetings between the Gows and The Bard, Robbie Burns, with his intricate, detailed stories. Alasdair would ably perform the most technically demanding of the Gow melodies. His ability to focus on the nuances of expression of the Gow compositions was mesmerizing. Sabhal Mòr Ostaig, Alasdair Fraser's short course, became the summer school of choice for many. Classroom dimensions limited, numbers spilling over, not a bad complaint to have. Additional teachers were needed, to satisfy the hordes.

The first moment I heard Alasdair play, I was spellbound. Might I be able to emulate his complex rhythms? I wanted to. Craving the ability to mimic Alasdair's syncopations, I appreciated the time he took to break it down. Alasdair was a very patient teacher. Did he recognise he had something special to offer other fiddlers? Did he know that fiddlers weren't already playing his rhythmic way? Very selfless, Alasdair, step by step, delivered his fiddle message. Musicians enthralled, achievement of these techniques not usually instant, Alasdair, waited. He watched, repeated and witnessed the learning process taking place in front of him. It was great to witness Alasdair taking delight, when his message sunk in and the class succeeded in absorbing some of Alasdair's magic. It was special, being there, being part of it, in many ways.

Alasdair had always been a very generous teacher, I remember. He freely delivered his techniques and stylistic tips. I had a thirst to learn his subtle techniques, the delicate ornamentations, the infectious effect of the sustained hammer-ons. How did Alasdair use dynamics? When did he choose to play softly? How did he play softly? When would he play loud and how could I learn? I had a thirst to know, to learn, all of it. You need to listen attentively to the music, watch the teacher carefully and feel the notes on the fingerboard. It is so vital to take all three disciplines on board if you want to emulate a player. Alasdair's approach was seductive. An active listener finds it easy to focus in on the details of how a musician's sound is achieved. You can see Alasdair playing quietly. You can hear him playing quietly. He is blessed with the ability to convey how it feels to play quietly. A good teacher asks his/her class how a particular sound is achieved. The learner has to come up with the answer. By thinking actively about how to create the sound, the learner is halfway there to being able to do it.

As much as I could, I would follow Alasdair on his occasional tours of Scotland. Resident in the USA for more than twenty five years, the opportunities to see Alasdair perform were few. I would make the most of attending his concerts and workshops whenever I could. I recognised the benefits of mimicking Alasdair's style as a pathway to developing and discovering my own. As a teacher, Alasdair was blessed with great patience. He broke the tunes down into manageable chunks. At the same time, he would keep the phrases within the context of the tune. Alasdair added the meat to the bare bones of the tune as he went along. Students would be challenged and enthused. A teacher's skill in delivering, is challenged as he inspires the learners. Alasdair's work was constantly innovative. He would delve deep into the oldest of Scotland's fiddle collections, researching the history of the traditional music, portraying artistic integrity and a respect for the authenticity of our heritage.

In the late 1980s and early 1990s, Alasdair was the fiddle player who, in my opinion, all young fiddlers with potential wanted to be like. Other than Aly Bain, I can't think of any other player of Scottish fiddle music, at that time, who connected with their audience or class in the way these players did. I'm sure others must have existed. I just wasn't aware personally of them. Alasdair and Aly had a special way of making the old tunes popular. They were able to demonstrate with ease that these ancient Highland melodies had rhythm and groove. Audiences were excited, fixated on Aly and Alasdair's command of their instrument. At times, the pair would take tunes that in their original form were technically quite manageable for a novice fiddle player to grasp. It's what these two players did with the tunes that was so alluring. They might gradually build up the tempo, to catch hold of the listeners attention. The trick was to feed the listener with a new gem each time the tune was played. Aly and Alasdair did that in spades. Perhaps an intricate variation on the repeat of the tune might emerge, as is common in Irish music. An innovative idea Alasdair might use is to play a low octave melody, holding the listener is his grip, an idea that would challenge students with new finger positions. Sometimes Alasdair would sustain individual notes in the higher octave. The strings would ring out as Alasdair toyed with the composer's intended rhythm of the tune. Listeners excited, the effect, unusual but highly impactful.

Alasdair and Aly were equally at home with the most technically demanding of tunes of the ancient as well as contemporary Scottish repertoires. They themselves have contributed enormously to the vast stock of Scottish tunes. Each player had an appreciation of the other's pedigree, Aly of Shetland heritage, Alasdair had a grasp of all traditions although originally focusing on classical violin, was master of the North East style. Each player complemented the other with ease and with subtlety when accompanying whoever was playing lead melody at the time. Aly's vast knowledge of repertoire coupled with Alasdair's indisputable ability to harmonize, highlighted and supported the melody, creating a rich and beautiful sound. Anyone would believe that countless hours had been spent achieving the result as a duo. However, often, these sessions were spontaneous, taking place late at night, in a nook or cranny of a bar somewhere, after a public performance.

Between them, Aly and Alasdair have amassed a vast number of albums. To date, Alasdair has recorded 17 albums, making appearances on a further 5 compilations. Aly, on the other hand, in addition to releasing 3 solo albums, has featured on no less than 56 recordings and appeared on 8 DVDs. While Aly's reputation is primarily as a performer, Alasdair is equally revered as a teacher. Quite in contrast to the late 80s and early 90s when the fiddle scene in Scotland and beyond was dominated by Bain and Fraser, the main stage today is shared amongst an abundance of fine players. Although some of these young, popular fiddlers are clearly inspired by players such as Aly and Alasdair, a lot more musicians focus their efforts on speed. While fast playing appeals to a particular audience, I believe a much wider audience appreciates a more controlled tempo. My personal opinion is, you can't beat rhythm when it comes to musicality. With rhythm comes control. Tempo needs to be controlled in order to maintain good rhythm. Give me rhythm over speed, any day. Perhaps biased, with the music of Cape Breton Island being a particular favourite, that specific style cannot be emulated if playing too fast.

Steady tempo I believe, allows time for deeper expression and demonstration of style. Style is another aspect in traditional music which is in danger of becoming lost or diluted when the emphasis is on speed. As my own playing was so strongly impressed upon by a number of styles such as Shetland, North East, Highland, West Coast, Donegal and Cape Breton, I was acutely aware of the need to control my tempo. It would simply not be possible to reproduce these styles without control, rhythm, lift and dynamics. All these key elements cannot be portrayed adequately or do the music justice when the tempo is too fast... well, that is unless you are Aly Bain. Another couple of speedsters I can think of who portray playing the fiddle as something that's as easy as brushing your teeth are fellow Caithnessians, Addie Harper Jnr. and Gordon Gunn. Both highly respected and well-travelled musicians in the traditional scene, their fingers fly around the fingerboard, effortlessly. Addie, a multi-instrumentalist coupled with Gordon's initial background in classical and Country music (I hope I am not wrong), between them boast a repertoire of American tunes as well as Scottish. Both players are equally at home composing intricate and demanding tunes and performing tunes at great speed on fiddle that at times might be more commonly associated with for example, the accordion. The two players traverse effortlessly throughout numerous octaves at the envy of fellow players and listeners alike.

This story brings together two very significant times in my life, my hospital stay in Ward 40 being one, the fiddle being the other. The irony is, we are presented nowadays in the media by documentaries for example telling us that the best neurosurgeon in the UK is at the National Hospital for Neurology and Neurosurgery in London. I strongly believe the best neurosurgeon is Mr David Currie at the ARI, mine of course, now retired. With an experience such as mine, who wouldn't pick their own surgeon? Of course, there's so much more to treatment and survival than the highly complex act of performing the surgery. The treatment begins upon the patient entering the hospital, to going through a battery of tests and procedures, the vitally important timing of the surgery, to the post-operative rest and recuperation and subsequent discharge from hospital and any follow-up outpatient appointments etc. I honestly don't believe that it is possible to receive better care than the treatment and care I received in Ward 40. I think my experience puts me in a position of making this judgement. Some may argue I don't have another neurosurgeon to compare Mr Currie with. True. I simply can't imagine better care, anywhere. The National Hospital for Neurology and Neurosurgery does boast over one hundred consultant neurosurgeons, while some doctors there are the only specialists in the UK in their particular field of neurosurgery. Mr Currie tells me he has performed twenty five aneurysm surgeries per year for the last twenty five years. That, I am certain is a vast number of extremely grateful and lucky people. He doesn't recall anyone returning for further aneurysm surgery...one point he makes in his aim to allay my anxiety. I am still working on digesting this point.

I craved knowledge of my particular condition. All the answers came from ARI. I'd come across the terms mortality and morbidity in my readings. These points required explanation. It turns out that both increase with the age of the patient; morbidity the condition the patient is in after the haemorrhage and mortality the death rate as a result of haemorrhage. What were the different treatments for burst aneurysm? I wanted to know. I'd already given mortality a big kiss. Having made my way out of the dark tunnel of negativity, having suffered I was now grateful. I'd come out the other side with a renewed hope. The books I consulted offered the answers. I didn't question the option suggested by my surgeon. I had faith in him performing the traditional method of open surgery. He believed that coiling would have been less suitable for me. I remember vaguely nodding in agreement. I think I was going with the flow. When I was ill, I didn't have the capacity to query or challenge the medics. If the neck of the aneurysm is particularly wide it can make coiling problematic. Was mine wide? I didn't know. Coiling fills the aneurysm with coils. The blood in the aneurysm is pushed back into the artery, where it should be. If the neck of the aneurysm is wide, the coils as they go in, can come back out again into the artery. Not safe. The age and condition of the patient after the haemorrhage are factors in determining the treatment method used. Coiling for me would have meant treatment in Edinburgh; an additional journey, an additional delay. Deemed a suitable candidate for open surgery, the decision was made. The sedative effects of the morphine medication I was receiving prevented me from questioning medical staff about the surgery. I was quite composed in my sedated state, partly desperate to have the treatment for fear of another haemorrhage occurring if I didn't have surgery soon and part relief at being saved from having to travel further to Edinburgh for coiling. My SAH happened on a Thursday. The operation went ahead the following Wednesday. With no bed space available in Edinburgh, the subject of treatment by coiling, the less invasive treatment was closed. Let me explain coiling. Putting it in context, you will appreciate the radical difference between the different surgery options to treat burst aneurysm. Coiling is commonly performed by a radiologist. Some aspects of the treatment are similar to the angiogram. Coiling is often more suitable for older patients who may be more at risk in coping with the open surgery. With age comes additional health issues. Lowering risk in an elderly patient might be key. Tiny platinum coils are fed through a narrow tube, a micro-catheter into the aneurysm. As the aneurysm is filled with the coils, so the blood content is diverted back into the artery, where it should be. The coils prevent blood from re-entering the aneurysm. Any blood already inside the aneurysm will clot onto the coil. Bleeding from the aneurysm should not occur and it should be prevented from enlarging. Developed only recently, coiling is becoming an increasingly common procedure option. A small majority of treatments for brain aneurysms in the USA are carried out by coiling. Over time, I believe, coils flatten out and patients need to undergo further treatment to have more coils inserted. For me, avoiding coiling meant one operation, permanent fix. After one out-patient follow-up appointment, I discovered I should need no additional monitoring. Coil patients, I believe, require ongoing monitoring. In addition, there may be the requirement of additional coils. Looking back, I can't be more thankful than for my treatment to be over.

I do believe I received the best treatment possible. As soon as the SAH was diagnosed, I was prescribed nimodipine. With a risk of epilepsy following SAH, the nimodipine would help to prevent further complications, before, during and after surgery. My surgeon carried out a craniotomy i.e. removed a bone flap through which he gained access to the area where the burst aneurysm was located. The special drill that is used to penetrate the skull automatically stops at precisely the right moment. With spring-loaded metal clip secured over the base of the neck of the aneurysm, the plan was to prevent aneurysm regrowth. It is critical that the clip is secured at the base of the aneurysm where it meets the artery so that no part of the aneurysm is between the clip and the artery. You can't risk aneurysm regrowth. This crucial detail was checked before completion of the surgery. The timing of the surgery was critical. Leaving it too late could risk a rebleed. My thirst for knowledge about SAH did not subside with time. As I hear the sad news of others who have been less fortunate than myself, Anita Roddick who established The Body Shop chain and Ariel Sharon, the former Israeli Prime Minister, it serves to remind me of how extremely lucky I have been to survive and fortunate to have been blessed by the skilled hands of Mr Currie and the Ward 40 staff who all played their part in saving me.

To complement my story of brain bleed is the story of my first visit to Sabhal Mòr Ostaig, the Gaelic College on the Isle of Skye. With no idea what to expect, I went with gut feeling. The signs were all there, after witnessing the virtuoso player on just two occasions previously, the course on Skye was going to be a blast. The year was 1987, just 3 years after Alasdair had established his California based course. Seeing Alasdair, alongside brother Iain, practising feverishly in the corner, backstage at Stromness Town Hall, had me hooked, instantly. Caithness Junior Fiddlers, my group, were the supporting act at the afternoon fiddlers rally. We all paused, huddled around the brothers who were squeezing in a last minute rehearsal, before taking to the stage at Orkney Folk Festival. I couldn't get enough of the rhythmically charged duos playing. Just a week later, Alasdair was back on stage, this time in my home town. Accompanied on piano by California native, the incredible Paul Machlis, in no time, I had decided exactly how I wanted to spend the last week in July that summer. On arriving at the course, an eager teenage fiddler, with only a few tunes under my belt, I was completely blown away. Overwhelmed and staggered at the experience to learn from Alasdair Fraser, I tried my best to hoover up everything he had to offer. The tuition was so intense. Alasdair obviously loved his work. Breaks were minimal, coffee on the go. Twenty five fiddlers eager to be taught; morning, afternoon and night, the learning never stopping, even when the nightly parties were over. We would drift off to sleep, letting our subconscious engrain the learning of the day. The master fiddler from California who had descended upon Skye continued to delight and enlighten the fervent class of fiddle enthusiasts. Alasdair was in his element. The group were the same. There was the added bonus of meeting some US fiddlers that week, familiar with Alasdair's teaching. They were regulars at his recently formed fiddle course in the California Redwoods. Not content with churning out a few tunes, Alasdair was keen to observe that the class had actively benefitted from his teachings.

On both these occasions; neurosurgery in Ward 40 and my first fiddle course on Skye I felt sure, it really doesn't get any better than this. I wouldn't go so far as to say that I am overtly religious. I was brought up to attend first of all, Sunday School and then when I was older, church. I used to pray – at the dinner table and before bed, a family ritual. Although I have let that lapse in recent decades. I would say that these days I am more spiritual than religious. Confident, I have received the best medical care there is, NHS Grampian, ARI, Ward 40. The team, led by Mr Currie; skilled, empathic and attentive. Medics; physiotherapist, doctors, nurses, anaesthetists and radiologists, rallying round in my hour of need. All the aforementioned staff believed I was safe. The care and support lasted well beyond my stay in hospital. Direct dial telephone number to the ward, you just have to ask. I did. An openness and willingness to take calls, any time. If I worried, and I did, I called. They answered. Immediate transfer or placement, on hold, until the best team member could support and allay my fears. What a comfort. Care, second to none. Made aware the décor was a little tired, no biggy when you are under the weather, more important issues to worry about. In the first few weeks after discharge, I would call the ward. Staff always on hand. Never had to wait long for an answer. Why did I call? Would the clip dislodge from the artery if I sneezed? Might the clip ping off the artery if I coughed? If I banged my head doing back stroke swimming, would the clip on my artery shift and cause a rebleed? Should I worry if I was hit on the head by a ball at the local leisure pool? You see, I didn't mean to fear. Mind in overdrive, it was easy to come up with scenarios. Many. Calls were never handled by a non-specialist on the ward. Always assigned to a doctor, each worry listened to, and a response without criticism or judgement. Trying to reduce the number of calls to what felt like my personal helpline, I admired and appreciated the care taken in referring me to more senior staff members. The telephone number still etched in my mind, I am thankful to no longer be dialling it. No doubt, the ward is thankful, too.

Did I feel guilty to be calling the number? Yes. On most occasions, the same doctor was called to the telephone. Grateful for the time, expertise and reassurance from him, concerned that with very little history, he knew he didn't need to ask my name. My time was more than up. His manner assured, I was afforded the opportunity to get everything off my chest before completing the calls. These examples, strengthen my case for ARI Ward 40, Mr Currie and team providing the best treatment and care possible. I tried not to abuse the good nature of the staff. My time was up. Operated on, sorted, fixed, appropriately drugged, cured. It was beyond the time I should have been calling for help. They had new emergencies to attend to. In parallel to my Ward 40 experience, I have also been fortunate to have experienced the best music instruction and inspiration from the greatest facilitator of learning. Alasdair practices, no problem at all, what he preaches! Ward 40, on the other hand, only provided the crème de la crème of neurosurgery. Twenty five aneurysm surgeries over twenty five years, Mr Currie? I was impressed, relieved. I had been in very safe hands.

Reticent to telephone Ward 40 on too many occasions, I happened upon The Brain & Spine Foundation. Not meaning to, rather, wanting to be free of the need, I found myself making multiple calls to The Brain & Spine Foundation Helpline. In the days and weeks following discharge from hospital, I had unlimited access to specialist neuroscience nurses. Don't take advantage, I encouraged myself. They listened and answered my queries about my condition, diagnosis and recovery – all the time acting swiftly, efficiently, professionally and calmly. While all conditions have a diagnosis that medical experts are familiar with, each individual's experience of their condition is different. From side effects, treatment, care, prognosis and recovery; physical and psychological, each of us experiences our illness differently. More than 50% of The Brain & Spine Foundation's income in the financial year ending 31 March 2022 came from donations and legacies. Fundraising accounted for 21.5% of the charity's income. The charity provides information, support and services and promotes understanding of neurological problems. In addition, the charity exists to support the advancement of medical research. Grants are available and/or loans, to individuals and to other charities with the same purpose. Funding is available also, to advance research into neurological disease and disorder and related fields. In 2022, 13,860 people were supported by a neuroscience nurse on their national helpline. Without judgement, the specialist nurses at The Brain & Spine Foundation, gave me confidence, my fears relaxed a little. A trust was built quite quick, easily. The nurses were obviously experienced and quick to determine the appropriate feedback. Always on hand to support and offer their words of comfort, it was important for me to reduce the calls to the service. I did. I'm not sure when. I don't remember how soon after first finding the service, did I stop calling for support. I had been lucky to find the service, by chance, while recuperating at my sister, Pauline's, while google searching. A great use of time. Believing me to be vulnerable, Pauline thought I was researching too much, so soon after being discharged. It was in the days of dial-up, no wifi then. Pauline in her office at work, the phoneline engaged, she knew what I was up to, searching for answers, seeking reassurance.

Ironically, I turned my back on the music. I felt certain I had experienced the best of Ward 40, not forgetting the vitally important role it plays in the lives of the people of the Highland and Grampian communities. I have made a point of using what I have learned with my music to support the ward in the best way I can. Gave up? I did, but not before recording a CD album with my great friend, Pete MacCallum, that would go on to raise several thousand pounds for the neurosurgical ward where my life was saved. It took many years hard work, and a lot of personal studying, to become a well-respected fiddle teacher. Abrupt almost, came to a standstill. There was no gradual going off of it. To say I despised the music, is a pretty close approximation. I don't know why. That seems so disrespectful. The very path I'd worked so hard on, had become like a nightmare. I was adamant, with no desire to play or teach, I receded from my love, the fiddle. You recognise, it all changed. So what on earth happened to alter that?

It was from performing and teaching that I made a living. Looking back to the time I was in the neurosurgical ward, I never once thought about my fiddle. I find that quite significant. I wasn't ever curious as to whether I would still be able to play; not while I was in Ward 40 anyway. During the weeks and months that followed my surgery, I never once had the desire to play the fiddle. I knew my passion for the music had ebbed away. I felt it almost immediately while recuperating at my parents' house, my sister's and my boyfriend's. Fiddling had become, indifferent to me. 180 degree shift. It was sudden, but, I contemplated. Didn't want to announce the end of my music too quick. First of all, I needed to come to terms with the decision, wait, think, confirm. And then, wait, think and confirm some more, before letting work, family, friends know. What would then fuel my recovery? The fiddle wasn't going to fill the void. The void was a result of the fiddle, on the back of the SAH. I'd given up playing. I was excited. Was I actually excited, or, was I subconsciously portraying that I was coping, putting on a front? I enjoyed it, the absence of fiddle playing in my life. I sighed with relief once the decision was made to quit fiddle.

My fiddle would never leave my sight. It would always be with me. That was the safest place for it to be. Never carelessly left lying around at a festival or a workshop, couldn't chance it. Instruments often abandoned, musicians trusting their fiddle or guitar will still be backstage or somewhere, waiting for them to return. When the fiddle wasn't in my hand and I wasn't playing it, it was in its precious case in my hand. An increasing number of instruments are stolen nowadays at festivals and music events. You can never be too careful. I have seen many instruments lying in cases backstage at gigs, neglected. Most cases look the same. Anyone could easily pick up a case and walk out the door without being challenged. Nobody was going to steal my pride and joy. But the feeling of not wanting to play came to me so suddenly and the days and weeks that went by I spent confirming with myself that was the case. It wasn't a decision I made on a whim. Initially I felt guilty but after a while I actually felt quite liberated and at the same time excited to wonder what would replace the fiddle in my life. Explaining the way I felt and the need I had to let go of something I had worked so hard to get good at, I struggled with. It took a lot of years for my talent to reveal itself.

Why was I happy to let go of my music? That's a difficult question to answer. Did I make the choice? At times I think, no. Was the decision made for me? I think it was. The music life was taken from me. That's what part of me believes. I don't ever feel my decision was about the music. As often as the voice that repeats the words 'brain haemorrhage' in my mind over and over, I would hear the mantra, 'give up the fiddle, stop playing'. New beginnings were beckoning me, urging me to start over, afresh, to do something new. I told myself, I wouldn't ever forget the music. I wouldn't ever forget how to play. It would be waiting, if I felt the need to go exploring it again. At the time, I was comfortable thinking about brain injury and my emotional recovery from that.

I Dream

Be positive. Need to maintain an acute awareness of that. Keep any negative thoughts out of my mind, I recounted. A strong mind and spirit will get me through this, I begged to feel. Getting the old me back was the plan. Invincible, that sense of feeling untouchable, I strived for it. Feeling immune to illness, I wanted that back. Sneaking up on me, out of the blue, illness had gotten me once. Now, the feeling was vulnerability. How could I shake that off? I tried. Prior to the haemorrhage, I felt exactly that. Invincible? Yes, that nothing would get me. A non-smoking, light drinker who enjoyed regular exercise, where was the risk? Lesson learned, you can never be too careful. Natural instinct tells you to feel safe. Everyone has a right to feel safe. Stress leads to negativity. Negativity can snowball, manifesting itself into illness. Best find a way to relax, I thought, take my mind off the illness. Were family members ruminating about my illness? I don't think so. From the very beginning, I was supported all the way. I would have done well to absorb some of their positivity, their confidence that I was safe.

I did try to remain positive. The fears hung around at the same time. How did I express my positivity? In the best way I knew how. When the chips were down, I got right back up and created what I did best. Ward 40 was my achievement, July 2006, less than a year after brain surgery. My coping mechanism was to make a CD. Unable to accept brain surgery and a two week hospital stay with a simple, thank you, I embarked on a fairly special project. I played fiddle, wrote tunes, engaged with musician friends, found a studio, leaned on those with the expertise needed to bring my project to life. We recorded an album to raise funds for the neurosurgical ward of my hospital. The chips had been down.

Making a recording as a fundraiser for ARI was a celebration of my way back to physical health. The emotional pain was still lingering a bit at the time. By selling the CD, I hoped that staff would buy books for medical students on the ward, blankets, chairs and any other resources needed. Proceeds from sales I remember, also went towards staff training. Again, this was over and above what was already provided by the NHS. It felt rewarding to give back in this way. I want to stress that once the costs of making the CD were recovered, all proceeds went to Ward 40. There was no personal, financial donation on my part. I understand, readers will have their views on donating money to the NHS. You may be thinking, I didn't have to pay back for the operation. I do know that. At the same time, you realise I didn't hand over my personal savings. It was a gesture of thanks. It was also a thank you to everyone who supported the project by purchasing a copy of the CD. Those aspects of the project helped in taking my mind off worries about suffering another bleed on the brain. Busy making, marketing and releasing the CD, kept me focused. Busy meant, reduced time to stress over brain aneurysms and risk of recurrence. It was all good.

I'm not sure when it was that on the 20th of every month, I began to forget. Until then, 20th of every month was a reminder of the date 'it' happened, the brain bleed. The mantra in my mind, began on 20th November 2005. It had been a month since the bleed. On 20th December, I woke to the mantra, that it had been two months since the bleed. The same 'awake dream' occurred on 20th of every month. When did it stop? I don't remember. It was years in. Do I hear you say, I need a psychiatrist? Raj? It was some kind of ritual. I was stuck in the cycle of remembering. Like a birthday, only it came around every month as well as year. Has the mantra actually stopped? No. I get caught out on days that aren't 20th of the month, reminded of the haemorrhage. Inevitably, I associate the 20th with the bleed. A part of my day will be spent thinking about it, wondering, will it happen again? When will it happen again? Shaking off thoughts that it will happen again, they are few and far between. I don't know, it's kind of like a fungus, niggling.

The niggle is under control. Well, as much as it's going to be, I think. Less of an obsession, more of an, I allow myself to think about 'that day'. Assigned time over, I get back to living life, free of the anxiety of the illness, until the demon returns. Medication would never be a fix, for me, no. Drugs? No. Not doing it. My reaction to remembering is less painful these days, much less. The physical pain associated with the anxiety no longer there, experience hovering, pay attention, be careful, watch out. My attempts to handle these anxieties manifest themselves through achievement. Setting goals and accomplishing them are what I thrive on. It's proof, I say, that I am coping. Some small personal targets I set, following recovery included; making minor adjustments to my gym routine, such as increased repetitions of a particular exercise; daring to raise my heart rate, to releasing the fundraising cd, to seeing this book in print, to securing an appointment with the neuropsychologist.

Turning a negative into a positive is valuable. When faced with adversity, be constructive. Switch on some optimism, set yourself a target, achieve that goal. Just like looking after the pennies and the pounds will look after themselves – one small goal achieved after another, will amount to big accomplishment. It's a survival tactic. Learn from misfortune and become better for it. This book was a challenge I set out to achieve from the darkness of my thunderclap headache. A couple of stories emerged in the early days, about my haemorrhage. These mainly centred on promoting my Ward 40 CD. Inevitably, the reason for the recording made press coverage. Another time, I succumbed to selling my story to a magazine, attracted by the small financial compensation, very small. The difference this time is, this book is all my own words, an honest account of exactly how it felt, to have the brain haemorrhage, the feelings, the sensations, pain, fear and recovery. Losing my granny, giving up my job as a music teacher, it's all in here. I didn't realise it at first. I thought the book idea in some ways would remain just that; an idea, a notion, a fantasy. I can make the analogy once again by relating to my music. Just as I believed a career in music would remain a dream, so too did I think getting this book published might remain the same.

A determined individual, I follow through on projects that I believe in, be they short term or long term. More comfortable being a team player than a leader, the book project demanded conviction, confidence and competence. Steep learning curve? Very. The left-brained me carefully and methodically poured over my story, the order at first, undecided. The chapters roughly, time about; brain haemorrhage, music career and repeated, with a smattering of family and friends in between. With family and friends so central at times, to my coping, it was unavoidable that they find their way into brain and music chapters and vice versa. Did you have questions about brain aneurysms before reading my book? Before reading my book, did you know that a bleed on the brain is a kind of stroke? In the USA, did you know that during post mortem, 1 in 50 people are found to have an unruptured aneurysm? Scary stuff. As the culmination of my thoughts and fears have been laid down, I hope you are enlightened about the subject of aneurysms. I hope some of your questions have been answered. If you have suffered a SAH, I wish you speedy recovery and a positive mindset. If other sufferers can relate to my story then I am reassured that what I have to say is valid. To anyone who has suffered an illness or knows of someone close to them who has gone through a trauma that has resulted in long term anxiety or post-traumatic stress disorder, I would hope that you can relate to my coping strategies. Coming to fruition, finally, 16 years after starting my book, publishing was beyond my wildest imagination. When and how did it come about, the book writing? I wasn't academically gifted as a child. I suppose I had a brief notion while hiking and cycling around the Cairngorm Mountains, Aviemore in July 2007. When I wasn't glued to the Wimbledon tennis tournament on TV between the rain showers, I somehow believed there might be time to write a book. In a week? At the time, I believed so. Didn't happen, but I'd made a good start. The location, the vast extremes of weather and the buzz around the mountains was exhilarating. Inspired but, where to begin? The diaries I had been keeping, the lists of key thoughts about my SAH and anxiety for a year and a half, were with me. The book is a culmination of my thoughts, anxieties and memories of the illness. It's also a celebration of my life as a musician as detailed in those diaries and journals, paper scraps, appointment cards and notebooks.

Visiting speaker for the day, Lorraine was introduced to our support group. The charity, Headway UK with branches all over the country, offer support to patients, families and carers of anyone who has suffered acquired brain injury. A lifestyle coach, Lorraine's topic of the day; Fear. Oh help. More specifically, she said the topic would be Body Pump fitness. Even bigger help. Anxiety levels rapidly rising, this was not going to go well for me. Comfort zone? No. Ready to get out of it? Definitely, no. With sweaty palms, anxiety and rising heart rate, the tension I felt was unbearable. Leave the room! I couldn't. Frozen to the spot, unable to eject myself, the torture continued. Was anyone aware? Unfortunately no. I tried not to listen. Didn't want to hear. I'd been there, once, doing body pump, when I suddenly had a brain haemorrhage. I wasn't ready to return. I was never going to be ready. Right there and then, the very thought of it, distressing, how could I stop myself from listening to what Lorraine had to say? End the topic, change the topic, break for a cup of tea, I urged, silently to myself. Talk over, I finally managed to make my escape. Time to leave the room? No, the building. Hope I managed to explain myself politely. Wouldn't want to appear rude.

Life coach, Lorraine, had also discussed press-ups. Tell yourself it's possible, she said. Just one, try it! All it takes is one. Let that be your mantra, encouraged Lorraine. Slow and steady, she advised, build up the number to work on your stamina. Attitude has a lot to do with ability. Just tell yourself it's possible. Adopting Lorraine's advice, I tried her suggestion and gave press-ups ago. Told myself I could do it and repeated Lorraine's words, internally, 'I can do 8 press-ups'. Okay, I struggled, but I did it. It was time to translate the same attitude to brain bleed and telling myself I wasn't going to have one.

Confident that I am safe to return to body pump both Raj and Mr Currie agree I should take the risk. Trust their judgement? Not me.

Not yet, at least. I choose not to take the gamble. Comfortable, instead, I chose alternative ways to keep fit. Building up time on the X-Training machine, I supplemented by fitness with swimming on Wednesdays. No need to modify lifestyle if an aneurysm is found, said Mr Currie. Although, he said, after a bleed on the brain he would recommend not heading a football for a year afterwards. I mean, I know he's the expert, but the words, brave and silly spring to mind, in equal measures.

Personal trainer, David Buchanan re-evaluated my fitness and boundaries. Originally struggling to do thirty minutes on the x-trainer, I was soon up to almost an hour. Enthusiasm in over-drive, I was spending almost 2 hours total in the gym, within a few short months of my recovery. Training sessions were soon increased to 3 times weekly. Swims upped to 80 lengths per session. Swim plus jacuzzi stretched to an hour. At 1600m, my swims I think were close to a mile.

Exercise in the morning, I found, set me up for the day. Less inclined to succumb to the temptation of bad food, a controlled diet went more easily hand-in-hand with an early workout. My strict ideals of a raw, organic diet, following hospital discharge, were eventually relaxed. Over time, a few carbohydrates snuck back in to my meal plans. Later unable to resist chocolate cake and cappuccino, did I think every time I succumbed to bad food, I might be encouraging another aneurysm to grow? I hate to admit it, but yes, if it hadn't already started.

Producing the Ward 40 CD was my way of showing that I was coping, recovering. By coincidence, I had prepared 40 fiddle tunes to perform at The North Atlantic Fiddle Convention, held in Aberdeen, July 2006. This was one of the few bookings I committed to, after my illness, performing and teaching fiddle at the five day event. Make a CD for the hospital, I thought. Why not? It could raise some much needed funds. It would enable me to maintain a link to the ward, allow me to ask questions, was I safe, are you sure I won't have another haemorrhage? Those sorts of questions. I'm sure the medical staff must have wished I would give it a rest, but they never complained. We found a studio near

Aberdeen, at a reduced rate. It was for charity after all. Accompanist Pete on guitar, and myself, we rehearsed for days. With minimal retakes at the popular studio, Pete and I were in and out within five hours, leaving sound engineer Neil Mathewson to finish producing the cd and making the master. I am indebted to the recording and post-production companies for reducing their fees. In addition, Kathryn Preston very generously waived her fee for the artwork. Photographers and good friends John Baikie and Malcolm Reavell donated the photographs for the album cover. A couple of press releases later and the CD was out. Private sales and shops agreeing to take the product resulted in several thousand pounds being raised in no time. A CD launch party in Skerray Village Hall, North West Sutherland raised a few hundred pounds. The significance of the venue? It was on the doorstep of my granny's family home we would visit when I was a child. Everyone donating their time for free, including musician friends; Veronique Nelson on fiddle and Iain Strachan on guitar. Performing to a full house, we were delighted to welcome audience members from as far away as Wick and Thurso in Caithness. With local community members donating raffle prizes and home baking, a total of over £700 was raised for Ward 40 that night. In addition, a number of audience members gave impromptu performances on traditional instruments. What a welcome, what a night. All in support of Ward 40, my special cause.

At that time, guitarist Pete had been a very good friend to me, for more than ten years. With an unrelenting stamina to play better, to make better chord arrangements and to support and sit behind the fiddle enabling the melody to shine, Pete was never one to upstage (take the limelight) any musician. A mature and loyal friend and musician, Pete was always sensitive to the dynamics of a performance. Equally at home, punching out strong rhythmic accompaniments, inspiring his melody player, Pete would complement more delicate tunes with appropriately subtle dynamics. Open to the influence of the melodic accents and off beats, Pete's playing was rhythmic, inspiring, complementary and captivating, rolled into one. He was quite the package, a great singer too. Subsequently the CD went on sale in a number of shops around the Highlands. By the summer of 2007, almost all of the 1000 CDs were sold, either on a wholesale or retail basis. The CD production costs financed by myself, once that amount had been recuperated, all proceeds were donated to Ward 40.

Why do I wrap myself in cotton wool? Why do I recognise risk and shy away? Will I always err on the side of caution? Would spending time with Karen Darke, lead me to willingly get out of my comfort zone? SAH in the past, will I return to lifting weights? No, but yes. Hand on heart, I can say, no more 10kg lifting for me. Maximum 2lb in each hand, just over 1kg. How long was it, before I felt brave enough to return to jogging? For years, I only walked, not believing it was safe to run. Initial fear that pounding the pavement might cause another aneurysm to grow, I think I must have read somewhere that tissue grows around the clip in my head. Would that help to prevent the clip from dislodging? I think I told myself, eventually, that it would. Repeated reassurances from my surgeon, no doubt, played a part too. The brain almost completely fills the space within the skull. Any notion I had, that the arteries were floating around, strained by the weight of the metal clip on my aneurysm, I have somehow managed to put to the back of my mind. Although I do jog, I can't say that I feel 100% safe. Working out within my comfort zone, do I allow my heart rate to increase? A little. Still feeling susceptible to aneurysms? Yes, more so than the general population. They are familial. We have a long family history of them. Back off, I say to them, at times. On my mind, as I write about them, here, I find myself becoming stern, urging them to beat a hasty retreat, leave me alone.

Performing the pike, star jump and summersault, I watched from the side lines. How long was it before I felt safe enough to join my nieces and nephews on their trampoline? I'm not sure. I am thankful to have overcome that hurdle though. My fitness trainer used to always tell me, get out of your comfort zone. Not wanting to burn out, if I paced myself, I could finish the class. He saw me as lazy. Illness behind me, back at the gym, I was thankful to be spared his teasing comments. Small milestones as opposed to breaking records, my motto. Increasing stamina and improving fitness levels during my Cairngorm book writing week, milestone fulfilled.

Prior to the brain haemorrhage, a solo trip to Canada, 1997. What took me there? Field visit for honours degree dissertation. Combining excitement with apprehension, I pushed myself out of my comfort zone. The social aspect of Bed & Breakfast accommodation, new to me. There's an anonymity staying in hotels. Still in my mid-20s, it brought me out of my shell. I gained an interest in meeting people, speaking to people. The field trip demanded that. Locals, I remember, were surprised, not to mention a little alarmed to discover, I was travelling alone. Ignorant to any risk, happy to say, I enjoyed a great tour of the Island, meeting great fiddle players and playing great music.

When I gave up my music career, was I subconsciously trying to get out of a rut? Was the haemorrhage the catalyst that forced me out of the rut? I have no memory of wanting to give the music up before I became ill. Quite the opposite. I had been on the cusp of focusing more on performance. Stretching myself to become a more rounded musician, exploring live performance would challenge me. My strength was in teaching. I felt completely in control of teaching fiddle. I wanted my performance capability to catch up. I had aspired to become a great fiddle player after visiting Cape Breton Island. The music on the island felt like home to me. It's ironic to think that 200 years before, Scottish emigrants had landed on the shores of Canada. The Scottish music and traditions were preserved there, in the Canadian Maritime region. It felt like the Scottish music of old was being reintroduced to me. This rhythmic, percussive style of music, no longer common in the Old Country (Scotland), I hoped to bring a little of it home with me to Scotland. The Cape Breton people were like family to me. They welcomed me into their homes. I was fed, offered a bed for a night or two, entertained by their music and hospitality. They showed a genuine interest in my musical style, at times remarking on the similarities between my playing and theirs. They recognised the Cape Breton influence on my playing. I was flattered. That gave me the confidence to play fiddle in their company. Intensely proud of their own style of fiddle music, the Cape Bretoners seemed quite purist. It was a daunting experience, daring to play. Would my music be accepted? On one occasion, I remember, rubber legs Rankin, Jimmy, I think, was his first name. He brought me some lobster. That was his way of saying he appreciated my fiddle playing. 10 or 15 years later, and Cape Breton bands were travelling back to Scotland. They were a proud nation, promoting their own brand of music. Cape Breton music has had an influence on the Scottish fiddle music today. Cape Bretoners stay true to their own style. The respect they maintain enables regional musical dialects to be preserved. Throughout my music career, the music of Cape Breton played an important role in keeping me focused on my love of playing. How extraordinary that music lost its place in my heart so immediately upon my return from the same island when, less than thirty six hours after returning home I suffered the SAH.

Musically, I was a bold, strong player. Music my voice, my way of communicating, my personality shone through in my music. Charismatic fiddle player, no self-esteem issues there. With a dedicated work ethic and a quiet resilience and bags of free-flowing musical ideas, music had been my calling. My confidence came out through the fiddle. My music was conspicuous. The delight I had for the fiddle evident. Listeners and learners alike could witness the confidence I had in my ability. Striking yet prominent, my music at times had finesse and delicacy. Complex and free my playing was methodical and at the same time, holistic. I liked to think of myself as a courageous fiddle player. Not satisfied to simply have a head full of melodies, compelled to tackle emotionally powerful slow airs.

What negatives were there when I shunned the fiddle? I struggled to notice. I saw change as opportunity. Releasing the Ward 40 CD, I saw as my one last big music send-off. Promoting the CD meant promoting the hospital, not myself, perfect. Promoting the Neurosurgery Ward at ARI spared me the usual inhibition and discomfort of self-promotion. And, there I was with a huge compliment, etched on the album cover, from one of Cape Breton's fiddle heroes, the now, late, great, Jerry Holland, who said this about my music, *The playing of Cape Breton Music won't die in Scotland with this lovely playing. She is a 'must hear'. It all without a doubt is magic.* If Jerry had lived a few more years, I hope he wouldn't have felt let down by my casting aside the music. I would like to think that he would have understood.

I dreamt of something taking the place of the fiddle in my life. My love for the fiddle sneaked up on me. By the age of about ten I decided I would like to learn to play. However, in 1979 in a small rural school there was no instrument instruction in fiddle. Two years later when I enrolled at Thurso High School I was able to put my name on a waiting list for tuition. It was another year before space became available. I'd made it onto the school timetable, with two other classmates. A shared lesson, once a week, for the next 5 years of school. The teaching and learning equated to 27 hours per year. The patience of waiting a few years for tuition, finally paid off. I didn't look back after that.

The fiddle had been my most treasured thing in the world. My initial instrument was a borrowed school fiddle, a Chinese production-line instrument. Next came a handmade instrument from Bruce Miller's Music Shop in Aberdeen, 1987. No matter the amount of effort I put into achieving a full and rich tone, the instrument simply wasn't up to it. 1990, Berkeley, California, my dad agreed to loan me the money to buy a Maggini copy fiddle that I discovered. I paid dad back. It took me a whole year. Within a secluded residential area, the shop was a fiddle player's heaven. Instruments were enticingly displayed, ceiling to floor, wall to wall and with a price range to suit all budgets. With mentor, Alasdair Fraser's endorsement of my selected two, we left the shop, permission to trial them both for a week. Instruments examined, tone scrutinised, I settled for the Maggini copy, an Italian design. Neither

Alasdair or I had been convinced of the authenticity of all the fake cracks of the Stradivarius. I wanted to like it, the Strad. The varnish, a rich dark brown, seemed more exotic to me, than the other instrument. But, it had to be about the sound. Looks weren't everything. Lucky though, the Maggini was not only pretty, it had the power in addition to the sweetness of tone I was looking for. The Maggini, with its trademark double purfling, confirmed our choice. Renowned for being a larger instrument, the strength of sound and tonal quality appealed to me. I could instantly reap the rewards of playing on a hugely better quality instrument than what I had been used to. Decision made, the Maggini was mine.

With sister Pauline, left, in Reay c1974

Taken 1990, granny (Mina Steven) left with grandma (Dolores Dickson)
Granny's cat Puddy who I adopted in 2004 when granny was too frail to take care of her.

Above left - Taken in 2003 by photographer John Baikie for my CD entitled The
Fiddle Workshop. Above right - With friend John Saunders on Scottish Border Pipes,
handmade by Hamish Moore, dad of my good friend and fellow musician Fin Moore.

NUDGED...

(Top) with Anne (L) & Alison,

(Middle Left) with Anne (L) & Alison,

(Middle Right) with Anne (R) & Alison,

(Bottom) with Anne (L) & Alison.

WARD 40
SCOTTISH FIDDLE & GUITAR

Karen Steven & Pete MacCallum

(Top) Christmas 2005 hair beginning to grow back,

(Middle) photo by John Baikie 2006,

(Bottom) with Anne (L) & Alison at NAFCo 2006

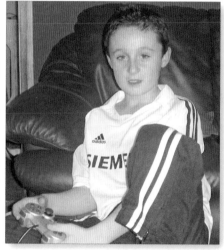

(Top Left) Niece Charlene on Island of Hoy, Orkney 2006, (Top Right) Nephew Darren c2007, (Middle) from left with sister Pauline, mum Christine & dad Eion, (Bottom Left) mum with her brother, my uncle Dainie, (Bottom Right) with sisters Pauline (L) & Maree (R)

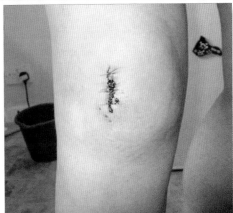

*(Top) with dad c2010, (Middle Left) baking with nephew Kyle, Jan. 2010,
(Middle Right) After first knee operation 2015, (Bottom) with piper Fin Moore (Dannsa)*

*(Top Left) taken 2022, (Top Right) from left, Caroline, Sandra & Fin (Dannsa) 2010,
(Bottom) from left Caroline, Mats, Sandra & Frank (Dannsa)*

(Top) downtime on Dannsa tour 2005 with, from left Sandra, Fin, Frank & singer Liz

(Bottom Left) Caroline, (Bottom Right) Sandra

(Top) with Gabe McVarish (Dannsa),
(Bottom) from left Caroline, Mats, Sandra & Frank (Dannsa) Photo by John Sikorski

All Change

What about my memory, immediately after the brain injury? Crystal clear in some places, will never forget. Patchy in others. No pain sensation, initially, the day the brain haemorrhage had occurred? The dominant souvenirs of the day; swirling dizziness, weakness, voice a whisper. Upstaging the thunderclap pain that's normally associated with SAH, it's hard to imagine a headache being swamped by a bit of dizziness. Memory wiped by a lack of oxygen to my brain, had there been pain when I first had the bleed? Unconsciousness brought on so rapidly, severity of the headache, overpowered, kind of hard to imagine. Is it healthy to try and encourage the gaps in my memory to be filled in? Not sure. I work through the story, from beginning to end. What do I expect? Recall of excruciating pain? Dull fog, head heavy on one side, a dizziness spinning in slow motion, they are the flash backs. The vast, black crater peppered with tiny, bright dots of red light floating in random patterns in the darkness. The fog closed in on me, the night 'it' happened. The denseness brought with it a fear that something sinister was happening. But no, no memory for severe headache at that time.

No room for fight or flight, the human body's instinct to survive. No energy in the tank, no adrenalin rush kicked in to help me tackle the situation. A complete loss of control, I had to surrender to John and colleagues at the gym to come to my rescue. In some ways I felt divorced from the situation, as though observing the experience from the outside. Caught up in the dream like state, unable to take part in the fight, I felt alone as my breath became weak. I grew fragile with worry, reliant on John.

The pain did come, I just don't remember it coming immediately. I was given a shot of morphine before leaving Raigmore hospital, Inverness. Had I been in pain? I don't know. Were the nurses anticipating the pain, trying to prevent it from coming on by administering painkillers? The headaches in Ward 40 were certainly of the unbearable type, continuously, until I was discharged home. The pain on the right side of my head was coupled with a constant numbness on the right side of my face. Imagine the numbness you feel when you are at the dentist? Only, it didn't wear off after a few hours. It came and went over a number of weeks. I remember, my jaw was stiff. At times, I would push a bit of food into my mouth, hope that it would disintegrate a bit, so I could swallow. The simple things we take for granted, eh? Chewing a bit of food. So, what had happened to affect my ability to eat? The secret lay in the trigeminal nerve. Located within the scalp, the surgeon had to cut through the nerve, in order to access the skull. With the nerve cut, chewing becomes compromised in the short-term. Small price to pay in the grand scheme of things.

Text books describe SAH as causing a sudden headache. Some patients feel small warning headaches in the days leading up to the main bleed. The headache is described as reaching its maximum intensity quite quickly. This does not correspond with my own memory. I was more aware of the vomiting than the headache being the dominant experience. The more severe the headache, the more severe the bleed. I regularly called for shots of morphine while in Ward 40. As this was some time after the initial bleed, I'm not sure whether it applies that the initial bleed itself was severe. With loss of consciousness wiping my memory of any initial pain, I just have the medical notes that confirm I was complaining of extreme headache. That would explain the mention of severe bleed.

After discharge. A car door closing, an unexplained creak from the house walls, I would find myself waking in the night, with a start. Reminded of the foreign body, the titanium clip attached to the flawed artery inside my head, I hoped it would remain secure. Worried that the momentary scare would raise my heart rate I would often imagine the spring-loaded clip pinging off. I waited, and waited. How could I shake off the anxiety? When would the tension and fear subside? At times, I would lie awake for hours, re-living the memory of the haemorrhage happening, until I drifted off to sleep again. Pre-occupied by the details of the event, I struggled to overcome the insomnia. What's the fix for that? Over time thankfully, although I would continue to wake during the night, the fixation on remembering the haemorrhage began to happen less. Fingers crossed, all digits crossed, in the hope all grizzly ghosts continue to remain at bay.

How do I cope? I used to imagine the clip was on an artery floating in a pool of brain fluid. Now reassured, I realise the brain itself takes up most of the space within the skull. The clip is wedged in and prevented from the danger of coming off? I hope so. I would pour over textbooks and academic websites to look for answers to my worries. Why am I the inquisitive one? Most patients who have survived SAH, accept the news when told they are safer now. Many survivors return to life as they knew it before, without question. Carers also often respond in a similar manner, believing the patient is safe. With the risk of rebleed and/or recurrence extremely rare, why then do I feel unsafe? Rare, think about it. To me, that means possible. It's happened once before, it can happen again. I think it's the family history of brain haemorrhage. What is it that eats me up with worry? Do others secretly harbour fears of what I am willing to discuss openly?

By the spring of 2006, I transitioned to a job in administration. Still with North Highland College, I felt relieved. Lucky to be accommodated by the college, I was able to hand the reigns of my music teaching job over to a former student. I recognised the passion in Eilidh (Scammell) that I had once had. She was the perfect substitute. I still maintained links to the music department in my new position, enrolling students and providing administrative support to music teaching staff. In addition to providing practical and academic instruction, by previous guise as music lecturer had included an admin function. My natural flair for administration included an ability to plan, organise and prioritise tasks, standing me in good stead with the college. I was thankful for the support I received from the college while I convalesced earlier in particular, from Assistant Principal of the college, Marcus Mennie.

The music took a back seat. But, personal and professional development were never going to. How would I stretch myself in the years following my illness? At times, I took to writing tunes although that came much later. To be a good painter, you need to practise painting regularly. To excel at writing, you need to write often. I believe in maps. Before the brain haemorrhage, my map was musical, highly practical, plenty of branches. A fan of mind mapping, Tony Buzan was an inspiration to me. I'm sure some of his ideas helped get me through my degree. Part taught, part self-taught, I hope that musicians coming upon my little book will be inspired. Here, I present to you with a snapshot of the highlights of my musical journey. Are you a musician? Have you been inspired? Was I a self-taught fiddle player? No. Formal, music education completed in 1987, I explored many aspects of traditional music at various short courses and camps around the UK and North America. I would say, my experience has been blended. Part tuition, part intuition, part active learning, part passive learning. Where was the value in passive learning? You can never underestimate passive experience. For me, that was simply the continued exposure to all kinds of traditional music growing up. Not always listening. Hearing is important too. A bit like a dream, when you are not consciously willing the story. I am optimistic that other musicians will draw inspiration from my experiences outlined in this book and hopefully find some ideas to help shape their careers.

In the years that followed my illness, I chased some new challenges. Following a different map, I sought new opportunities. I practiced writing and I undertook courses. While I brought many strengths to my role as administrator at North Highland College, I recognised there was more that could be achieved. I had spent ten years in music. Would I spend the next ten in administration? With a will to keep my soul alive, I endeavoured to make new plans, hopes and dreams. Simply getting by was never in the equation. At times, I was impatient, I think. With my music, I had taken my time. I had no choice. I felt like I had been a painfully slow learner. Slow and steady had worked for me in the past. I was intrigued now, open to change. Armed with the willpower to explore alternatives to music, I realised the importance of happiness. In terms of our health, we don't know what's in store for us. No matter how fearful I was of suffering another SAH, that could not stop me from living life. How did I demonstrate to family that I was coping? Taking my nieces on holiday was a big step for me. Having the responsibility of looking after them meant my mind was focused on them. Is what I am saying, if I am kept busy, my mind will be distracted from thinking about brain haemorrhages? On that holiday, for those few days, I was busy, yes, only it was thinking about Charlene and Ashlyne and planning activities for them. I didn't consciously make the connection that there might have been some kind of therapy in keeping busy, looking after my nieces. I'm sure, at the time, thoughts of my illness were in the back of my mind. My focus was on the girls, making sure they had a great time. They target paintballed, rode on quad bikes and braved roller coaster rides. Before the SAH I would have joined them. Sensitive to my health concerns, but feeling invincible themselves, I feel lucky to be their aunt, very. We took a boat trip, two boat trips; one out into the North Sea to the Orkney Islands, the other, around Scapa Flow. We cycled, hiked and cycled some more. No children myself. Didn't need any. They were it, for me. I valued the time we spent together, when they were growing up; craft days, baking days, treats (within affordability and sensibility) and a few holidays thrown in, whether at my houses in Alness, the family caravan in Dornoch or hotels around Scotland and the Orkneys. I would relish the opportunities to treat my nieces and nephews to holidays. I would take them, one, two sometimes three at a time over the years. When not having them to stay at my house, the trips included travelling all over Scotland and to Benidorm, not forgetting Mediterranean cruise.

Reliance on the Glue

My memory might have been a mix of vivid and ropey, dad's on the other hand, was lucid. I could be forgiven, for not being clearheaded, in Ward 40, yes? Steadfast reliability and profound and unremitting faith in my neurosurgeon, Mr Currie, that was my dad. The man knows what he is doing, dad would say. I can imagine my dad, asking, and at the same time telling Mr Currie, she's going to be okay, isn't she? Willing the surgeon to agree with him, I'm sure dad was looking for the reassurance that I would come through the surgery. A strong bond and belief in Mr Currie, I'm not sure my dad ever doubted I would be okay. Was that the sort of mantra he had? If he recited the faith, he would be willing it to be true? He had a quiet confidence, my dad. In life I mean. He passed away recently, December 2021. Just as he had been with me in my greatest hour of need, I valued the opportunity shared with my mum, my sisters and brother, to be with him, in the days leading up to his passing. It was a comfort to the whole family I think, that we could go on that final bit of dad's living journey with him. We witnessed dad being freed of any strains, stress, frustration and tension as his demeaner became calm, accepting, comfortable. Wonderfully free of the need for any undesirable drugs in the latter stages, dad didn't appear to be a slave to the disease, calmly and quietly holding our hands, two at a time, according to covid requirements. A dignified passing, his life lasting longer thanks to the NHS coming to dad's rescue some months previously. It wasn't easy to know what to say to dad in his final days and hours. Although quite hearing impaired, they do say the final sense we are left with is our hearing. Might dad's hearing have been enhanced, magically, towards the end? I don't know. I do remember one of the last things I said to him, Can you imagine, dad, it's raining AND the sun is shining. That was the view we had, from his palliative care window. It was December. It was a rainy day and the sun was shining. And then, the very last thing I said, before he passed was, that I was just going back to the house for dinner and I would see him later that night. Before I got the chance to see him again, he had passed away. I did speak to him again though. It was a few days later. I went to the funeral home to give him one last haircut, the one that in life, his illness would not allow me to give. I even apologised to him, for bumping into his nose, while I crossed over to trim his eyebrow. Dad always liked his eyebrows shaped. Haha, nothing fancy, just combed smooth and cut straight across and then combed back into shape. Dressed in his favourite suit of mum's, ready for a few pictures and with mum's consent, I took some photos of dad for his family who live in the south, granny's nieces, my dad's first cousins.

Back to 2005 for a moment and, no matter the number of times I would initiate the topic of brain haemorrhage, dad was certain, if Mr Currie said I would be fine, after surgery, then I would be fine. I should trust him, he intimated. He incited me to have confidence in our NHS. Which reminds me of a tune I once composed for dad, *Incitement for a Dormant Elkavox*. The Elkavox was an electronic accordion that dad had treated himself to some years before. I don't know, did he go off accordion playing? Had the instrument latterly become a bit heavy for him? Dad had been a great player, self-taught. With the electronics within the box, he was able to create a kind of piano accompaniment sound. In a way, the effect was one-man-band. It had been a while since I'd heard dad play accordion. I composed the tune for dad in the hope that it might encourage him to play his accordion again. He did play again, but on a smaller, more portable sized accordion. My numerous, in depth discussions with dad, about brain aneurysms, treatment and recovery raised many questions. While I agonised over all the possible answers, dad confidently preached from the same book as my lifesaver, Mr Currie. Dad trusted Mr Currie intuitively. Is it wise to trust, when you don't know a person? When you have just met someone, should you trust? I remember, Dr. Raj Persaud (my front-cover book endorser) telling me once, you should never trust immediately. Trust should be gained over time. In day to day life, yes I can hear my dad say but this was different, very different. We had put my life in the hands of the skilled and experienced one. This had to be a short-cut to trust. Do I feel guilt when I worry about my safety from aneurysms? Yes. I feel a little ashamed. At times I think it's not fair of me to react in this way. Is it deliberate? No, I don't think so. I would love to lose the lingering doubt. Did I lack trust in neurosurgeon, Mr Currie? Quite the opposite, I'm sure. Just a couple of questions after reading the consent form. Read it thoroughly, I told myself. Got to know what's going to happen, I reminded myself. Satisfied I understood the procedure and any associated risks, I signed. I remember, I sensed being rushed. There seemed to be an urgency for me to sign. Calmly, I pointed out, I was reading through the form, didn't want to sign straight away. I felt that would be ignorant. The feelings of mistrust came after, not before. Agreeing to the surgery was the easy bit. The risk of doing nothing would be a ticking time bomb to disaster. Mistrust afterwards? No, more of an anxiety for my safety. I felt it was a disrespect of my dad. Where was the glass-half-full mentality, the positive nature I claimed to have? Hopefully I can be forgiven for not coping too well on that occasion. Was dad secretly reiterating the words of the neurosurgeon, in his attempt to help me feel safe? Was dad concerned for my safety? I'm sure he must have been worried. At no time did dad show any weakness or vulnerability. He remained strong, focused and unflinchingly trustworthy that once the surgery was behind me, all would continue to go well. Parents worry. It comes with the territory. I was lucky to have my family's presence, strength and support.

Fourteen days dad spent in the ward with me. His mind keenly alert to the possible dangers of my situation, my body was sedated and at peace, obedient and unquestioning, except that is, for the dollop of worry questions you already know of. I suspect my dad presented Mr Currie with a number of questions during this time, while I was protected from these difficult and sensitive enquiries. And then, 9 days after I was admitted to hospital, granny died. 29th October. I think it was mum who delivered the news. Just like that. She said it. For the duration of my hospital stay, I remember noticing how calm and composed mum appeared. On the inside, her stomach must have been in knots. Devastated, at least I would have been, if not for the morphine, dulling any emotional outburst. No display of grief or tears. Why didn't I react? Why couldn't I react? It was the drug, prescribed for the physical pain, but doing a job on the emotional pain too. The matriarch of our family, my best friend, gone. I would never see her again. Her funeral service held, two days before we arrived home from ARI. Prepared in a way, we'd had a scare the previous month, when granny's health had taken a turn for the worst. At 93, granny had been the oldest in the family. Of Mackay pedigree, granny had grown up on a tiny north Atlantic island. The family livelihood had been crofting and fishing. By 1938, all families had left the island, settling in a nearby, small township on the north mainland of Scotland. The incentive, £100 per family from the Countess of Sutherland and a property to rent. Keeping the tenancy for 50 years would allow families to take ownership. The house, in Torrisdale, I remembered visiting when I was tiny. Granny's parents, Great-grandad and great-granny, I can visualise them now, greeting us outside when we would visit. Great-grandad had a walking stick. He would tap us on the backs of the legs, gently, as we entered the house. It was as though he was counting us, rounding up the sheep to be dipped. I think I was 2 years old when he passed away, maybe 3. Being the eldest child in the family, and for nursing both her parents in their final years, the north west family home was left to granny.

Life on the island, growing up, had been hard. The oldest of 5 siblings, granny, at times, would be called upon to rescue a sheep from some inhospitable bit of the island, stuck on a rocky promontory, or a heavy ewe (female sheep) trapped in the icy water. Salient memories of stories etched in her mind from the old days, granny would describe in great detail the hardship faced by her family. Washing heavy wool blankets by hand, hanging them out in the open, exposed field beside the house to dry, salting the fish was another arduous task assumed of the oldest child. Tied by their tails, in pairs, the fish were suspended from a wooden pole fixed across a geo (a steep rocky inlet), naturally salted by the sea crashing against the rocks. Fish stored in barrels, salt-herring and potatoes, the family staple diet. Surviving 3 of her younger siblings, I wanted granny to last forever.

The torture that dad must have endured when granny died, would have been agonising. Without morphine to help his pain, dad maintained a vigil for me as I waited for surgery. No doubt he was torn. As granny's time was nearly up, would he stay with me or be with granny? He chose me. I was unaware of her death, initially. The family kept the news from me, not wanting to stress me further, so soon after surgery. My sisters had left on the day of my operation. They visited granny. She wasn't without family, but they wished they could have been with her for longer. Dad, along with mum, had been granny's rock for years. Deprived of final visits, they prayed, while staying in hospital, with me. While the rest of the family mourned the loss of granny, the morphine ensured I selfishly was allowed to focus on me. Had I been aware of granny so close to dying, I would have been destroyed. Knowing how close I was to granny, the family didn't want to risk telling me the news. Unaware, I was left to concentrate on my thoughts of the pain and worry at being alone at night in my private ward. My mood wasn't up. It wasn't down. It was like a bland, 'middle of the road'. The morphine taking away the strain.

What was going through my dad's mind as I lay in hospital. I don't know. I didn't ask him. I couldn't ask him. It must have been unbearable for him to not be with my dying granny. But, worry he would have, wondering how I might cope, if he left to go to granny's funeral. I can only imagine he was torn. Imagine, not getting to your own mother's funeral. I would have totally understood if he had gone. I wish he had given me the chance to say, go. As soon as my operation was over, I felt a degree of safety. Initially, anyway. I think, because it maybe hadn't registered, how life-threatening the SAH had been. Discharge day came. I wasn't ready to leave. Hospital the safest place, let me stay until Christmas, I begged. No such luck. My time was up. Great news, I was deemed safe to go. Armed with a giant bag of meds; paracetamol and morphine, plus letter of instructions, we made for the train journey north. The car had gone north with my sisters a few days earlier. Give me morphine by injection, any day, over the tablets. The taste alone, of the pills was enough to ensure I wouldn't take any more than I needed to, or was safe.

Conscience finally caught up with me, the effects of the morphine gone, I was floored at the news of granny's death. Not being a part of her final days was excruciating. Had I let her down? No, she would have understood. Ever selfless, granny had meant everything to me. Nobody more mentally strong, frustrated by physical weakness, it was just a matter of time. Unable to cope with another blood transfusion, they took hours to administer, her Christian faith, I think, would have taken her to Davviday, my grandpa. Care home last resort, granny had lived independently for 18 years after losing grandpa. Loved by all the family and we by her, I had nothing but admiration for my bestie who would still help out at our B&B, the one she had established 60 years earlier. She would be well into her 80s, cleaning dishes, cleaning floors. Head down, jobs done, granny wasn't there to socialise. Not a visitor herself, she cherished receiving visitors. Animal lover, she truly was remarkable. Could she not have held on? Waited for me? To come home from hospital? Be the one who was there at the end? Granny had always been there for me, for our whole family. It felt like we had let her down. My tears didn't flow when granny passed away. The morphine made sure of that. I couldn't understand why her funeral wasn't delayed for a couple of days. Could it not have waited until the family came home from hospital? At the time, I didn't query it. I think we were all in shock. It wasn't discussed. Whose idea was it, to have granny's funeral service filmed, so we could take part, in our own private way? I don't remember. I would like to think it was mine. It didn't seem right the funeral going ahead without us. It wasn't right. Unable to change the ending, we have our memories. And, boy, they were special.

Trademark Highlander, granny was an excellent cook and baker. Recipes adapted to a handful of this and a handful of that. The success of baking, down to a precise science, it amazed me, the quality of granny's bakes, without the precise use of weighing scales. Granny had obviously honed her skills over the years, with plenty of practice in Caberfeidh House Hotel – the business she established with grandpa (Davvidy). She had all the modern utensils, even boasting a microwave oven in the 1950s, long before they were commonplace. No doubt, Davviday had treated her to one. I remember, the door opened down. Pancakes and oven scones; delicious, light, fluffy. Fresh cream featured in so many of her recipes. Her Eve's pudding, with vibrantly yellow sponge made with eggs of the highest quality, granny's baking would rival the best of any professional chefs attempts. Eyesight deteriorated, hearing virtually non-existent, shopping became a chore for granny in her twilight years. Latterly housebound, but granny had much to say on politics, religion and the latest world affairs. Never neglecting her skincare regime however, granny would diligently apply good quality moisturising face creams every day. Not dry, not oily, her skin was blemish-free, until her final weeks in life. Protected from the elements, granny's skin maintained a youthful quality to it. Well informed, granny rigorously offered her opinions on all topics of conversation. A strong believer in keeping her mind active, granny maintained a sharp wit and zealous interest in her family, particularly her grand-children and great grand-children. Both her short and long term memory served her well until the end. A great lover of traditional music and dance, granny couldn't resist getting up and dancing a Highland Schottische when I played fiddle. As well as her mind, her heart was strong. Even at 92 years old, she was light on her feet, lilting around the floor, pointing her toes, my mum, partnering her.

When the chips were down, who would I normally call on? Eldest sister, Pauline. Alerted to my emergency, but not until the morning after, Pauline dropped everything at work. No questions asked, worry in overdrive, Pauline rounded up the family. She had heard I was in Raigmore hospital, soon to be transferred to the neurosurgical ward at ARI. Family members quickly rallied round, making arrangements for all my nieces and nephews, taken in by Pauline's parents-in-law. Childcare sorted and children settled, the drive could begin. Plans for Charlene's birthday would have to wait. Maintaining as normal a routine as possible was the plan, with the children making the 40 mile round trip daily to school while their mums were away. Detour to granny's care home in Wick first, Pauline took ownership of delivering the news. The details of my illness masked. Didn't want granny to worry. That's quite a headache, granny must have thought. With the family now gone, care home staff stepped up support for granny. With no time to waste, mum, dad, Pauline and youngest sister, Maree, made the long journey south to ARI. Arriving after dark, they weren't helped by poor road conditions, which to this day, still don't seem to have improved any.

The many special letters and cards from my darling nieces and nephews bore testament to their awareness of my situation and concern. I'll never forget them thinking of me at this time.

Topic of conversation on the journey, no doubt had been mum's sister and nephew. Both passing away at age 35 and 30 respectively, and me entrenched in hospital with what was believed to be the same complaint, chats must have comprised lots of questions but no answers. Anxiety of family medical history coupled with knowledge of potential outcome for me, a huge worry, my family's long journey seemed even longer. The need to get to their destination, heightened. Every driving minute felt like ten. Might they be too late? Had medical knowledge advanced since Honora and Ian's brain haemorrhages? Might their bleeds have been operable if they had happened more recently? Best not to ruminate. Couldn't change the outcome for them. Medical advancements, Karen will be fine, thought Pauline, prayed Pauline.

Concern and disbelief, thought Pauline, at the news I was in hospital. Are you joking?, no doubt she said. Where was the bleed?, Pauline queried. Taking in such unexpected news, a shock, I'm sure the family checked and checked again. Did they hear the news correctly? With the diagnosis of brain bleed confirmed, everyone had to keep their s..t together, at least until they arrived in Aberdeen at my bedside. With a family history of brain haemorrhage comes a greater risk to other relatives. I later worried for them; my mum, dad, sisters and brother. Bizarrely and in spite of statistics, they all didn't seem at all concerned of the risks. With the focus of anxiety firmly fixed on me, any concern for their own safety would have waited until later. Committed to visiting granny every day, she would realise that something was up if mum and dad weren't there. No family visits, everyone south to be with Karen. Normally so alert, if granny was that close to passing away, hopefully she was too weak to take in the news that I was sick. I remember the time granny thought her house was on fire. She sensed it. Shopping trip cut short, she urged grandpa, let's go home immediately. They arrived back to find their chimney had gone on fire. Just in time, they were able to act and get it put out. On another occasion, I remember granny telling me, she saw her younger sister, from the spirit world, standing at the end of her bed. Granny wasn't afraid. I think it was a comfort to her. She told me she hadn't been spooked by seeing her sister's ghost.

My niece and nephew, Charlene and Darren are Pauline's rock, and she theirs. They are mine too. A great source of comfort for me, as I lay still in Ward 40; waiting, wondering, worrying, Pauline left her two children in the care of granny Gills. Pauline cherishes Charlene and Darren, yet, there she was, prioritising me. The kids were young, age 10 and 9 at the time. Let me describe Pauline. Hoarder? Yes, of all things, clothing. Not only that, shoes and handbags too. Does she conform to national statistics and wear just 20% of her wardrobe? Nope, Pauline falls into the category of wearing 100% of her clothing clutter. Loves a splash of colour, Pauline has no shortage of all things material; casual AND smart. A wide selection of classic monochrome and bright, colourful, outfits, all occasions catered for. She has no need to buy a new outfit for special events. So many to choose from at home, oh go on then, what harm is another one, Pauline would say.

Distress in her mum's voice, Charlene's first thought was that something had happened to old-gran. With a hospital nearby, why the need for Karen to go to Aberdeen, Charlene worried. 11th birthday, just a few days away, Charlene wanted her mum home. At the same time, the mature side of my niece wanted her mum to stay with me in hospital. You were fragile and very slow at moving, said Charlene, when I came home from hospital. On a scale of 1 to 10, with 10 being very worried, Charlene chose a 7 about me. Definitely an old head on young shoulders, Charlene didn't think anything would happen but she worried that I didn't look well. Charlene shares a similar robust nature to her mum, Pauline - a stamina, that resilience and invincibility that protects. Charlene's brother Darren on the other hand, you might say is more in touch with his emotional side and was worried I might die. While admiring and loving them both, I enjoy that Darren is comfortable wearing his heart on his sleeve. On saying that, we also have no shortage of laughs together, even now.

Pauline is the emotional figure in our family, always has been. I'm sure anyone who happened to be in the hospital corridor when Pauline was around, witnessed her episodes of tears and fears. I appreciate her all the more for protecting me from seeing her vulnerable side. You know what they say about honesty, right? I wouldn't have minded her breaking down in front of me. She's always been emotional, Pauline. Cries at fiction on tv. Never was my way. In fact, in my morphine induced state I'm not sure I would have comprehended the reason for Pauline's outbursts. I know that I for one could not have contained my feelings so admirably in the way that she handled it had our roles been reversed. In truth, I think our mum demanded that everyone hold it together, in front of me. No signs of weakness allowed. In fact, had she broken down in front of me, I feel certain my thought would have been, what's wrong with Pauline?

Not me! Was this reason for me being in hospital something serious? For sure, I think I would have been perturbed.

Quite staggered to find all my family with me in hospital, like I've said already, I'm not sure I was aware of the seriousness of my condition. Obviously we had been told the news that I'd had a brain haemorrhage. Initially terrified due to family history of brain haemorrhage, I think I transitioned to feeling support, a special treatment, in a way, at ARI. Surrounded by family, friends AND doctors and nurses, at ARI, I felt quite spoiled, safe almost. Must have been the morphine drug again, playing tricks, making me feel normal. My sense of the real world, that's what the morphine had removed. Ensconced in Ward 40, ARI, I think I felt as though the worst was over. Everything was going to be okay, wasn't it? Periodic mention of angiogram, what? Explain please? Surgery was mentioned too. What? No? Surely not? Within a few days, I began to panic. No progress. Ah, it was the weekend. Condition stable, we waited. Immediate family still visiting, I was confused. What was going on? It wasn't that bad was it? The headache? Routine occurrence, several times a day, the visits quickly seemed a standard fixture. Did my subconscious know that something was up? I began to look for visitors earlier and earlier each day. Amazing, the power of a bit of company. A little hush hush on the morbidity front (my health condition), I thought. As an attempt to prevent me from over-reacting or freaking out, I was spared any discussion of brain surgery. No doubt, mum's insistence. No breaking down in front of Karen allowed. Meanwhile everyone around me must have been even more worried. They were in on the chat. They knew what was to come. In a way, it was worse for them. I was worried about the wait, for fear of something sinister happening before the hospital had the chance to save me. But between worries of these serious and vital landmarks of my time in hospital I was slightly bewildered at the presence of my immediate family on such an ongoing basis.

Liveliest member of the family, never short of a word or 500, Maree. Youngest in the family, I'd never seen her this quiet before. In shock no doubt, that the one who should be least likely to fall ill, had done just that. Clean living, independent, almost tee-total, non-smoking me, struck down by a terrifying illness? Yes, it had been confirmed. I'm not sure when it really registered with Maree. Just goes to show, anything can happen to anyone at any time. So unusually quiet, but Maree's silence didn't bother me. The presence of visitors, any visitors was a power of support. Didn't need to be chin-wagging all the time. Plenty others were able to keep my spirits up. Silent company adequately took the place of conversation, at times. Maree included. The presence of family, plus friends; Anne, Wendy and Alison filled the void when there was no conversation, just by being there. And later, Sheila, Ward and Grant, plus box of homemade biscuits from Sheila's mum. My severe loss of appetite meant that box of biscuits lasted the longest time ever. They managed to stay crunchy until the last one came out of the box. I remember that much. Plenty would agree, Maree would never normally be stuck for conversation. To be honest, did I actually notice? Not sure that I did. On reflection, I probably did.

Youngest nephew, Kyle, I remember, he was never one to play kids games or with toys much. While he enjoyed cooking and baking with his aunt, Kyle was more at home mixing cement or doing jobs on his grandparents farm. I remember, Kyle was a great help to me in Alness once, transplanting my Asiatic Lily from the patio to a corner in the back garden. Next he shifted the patio slabs, before helping his dad to cement them in, in their new location, the old patio ready for the new conservatory build. A tough cookie, Kyle wasn't fazed by the challenge of manual work. He must have been 6, no older than 7 at the time. Come closer I encouraged him, after I came home from hospital. Don't be afraid to give me a hug. I wanted to give him a cuddle too. At just 7 years old, Kyle had been scared to even speak on the phone with me. I did my best to comfort him reassuring him that it wouldn't hurt me for him to come near. A firm believer that stresses and strains should be borne by adults, I did what I could to make the kids feel secure. I am deeply indebted to my parents, siblings, nieces and nephews who were so understanding of my needs.

The 5 children missing their mums, my sisters set off for home, after I came round from the operation. They also wanted to see granny one last time. I am indebted to Pauline and Maree for being with granny in her final hours. If only I could have been with her, be the one to share her last hours with her. Had I made it home in time to see her, I feel certain she would have extracted from me the reason for my previous absence. In spite of her severely impaired vision, I believe she would have seen the evidence that I'd been in hospital, without me having to explain; the scar, the weight loss, my loss of hair. I remember visiting granny once in her care home and she commented on a tiny speck of white fluff on the cardigan I was wearing. The white fluff was from her cat Puddy; her cat I'd warmly agreed to adopt when she was no longer fit to care for her. I was quite startled to think she could see something so tiny, yet be unable to see well enough to even write her own name. If you had asked granny at the time, I'm sure she would have said that God had let her see it. Granny adored her cat Puddy. Spoiled, Puddy had lived on a diet of freshly steamed white fish and salmon on alternate days and lactose free cat milk and water. Puddy knew her time was up. She took herself away to a quiet spot and died exactly two months after granny on the 29th December 2005, age 20. In floods of tears this time, the effects of the morphine long since gone, I felt so guilty at not being able to feel that when granny died.

My avid dependable rocks are my friends in Aberdeen; Alison, my free-spirited active angel forever supportive, great company, even in my darkest hour. Her laughter, her smile, Alison reaches out and attracts the attention of those around her with ease. Sense of humour, this time, in check, I relied on Alison for comfort and her warm personality. Like my mum, Alison provided some much needed chat, both doing it effortlessly. Alison, dependable, her company, crucial in my time of need. No strangers to loss and heartache, the two of them. Their presence, unfaltering. In my helpless state, the precious two of them were never short of something to say. How do they do that? Know what to say, how to say it? Plugging silent gaps at exactly the right time.

Awkward? Never. Silences filled with meaningful conversation and heartfelt words, I felt honoured. Grateful for a moment or two to clear my mind of selfish thoughts of my condition. Each visit ended with me looking ahead eagerly to when they would return and ease my burden in Ward 40, simply by being there.

My dear friend Anne who I met in 1993, ironically through music, remained a true and constant support. That summer on midgie infested Isle of Skye in a blue and white marquee tent we discovered our common interest and fascination for all things Scottish and Cape Breton in music. A petite red-head with the biggest heart and most talented, nimble fingers on piano, Anne and I would spend every available opportunity jamming on the fiddle and keyboard. Later that year I visited Anne in Aberdeen when we attended the Fiddles on Fire concert. From then on our friendship was cemented and we continued to meet for tunes and chats. While a student at the University of Aberdeen, I was lucky, Anne and I would regularly meet up for lunch or to play tunes in her ceilidh band. While other students toiled away stacking shelves in supermarkets to supplement their university existence, I enjoyed the luxury of playing in Anne's band for weddings and ceilidhs. A challenge at first, I soon got to grips with the repertoire, learning all the sets by heart. Our friends Pete, Alison and Jean Ann were also in the band. I strongly believe we were so lucky to be close friends on a personal level as well as compatible musically. I do believe that's a rare combination indeed. Anne was the kind of person who always said *yes* or *I'll think about it* and then *yes*. She was definitely from glass half full stock. As I settled in at the University of Aberdeen, Anne took me under her wing. Our friendship developed as we expanded our common repertoire of Highland tunes. Although a Geordie by birth, Anne lived, worked and partied for a number of years in Scotland, a childhood dream she managed to fulfil. She was blessed with a tremendous stamina to do her best for her family, for the environment and for herself. Anne ever generous with her time would happily spend hours creating innovative arrangements of tunes and sets of tunes we had learned from Alasdair Fraser, Buddy MacMaster or nicked from a Michael Flatley (Lord of the Dance) recording.

Mum has had a lot of heartache to deal with in life. As multiple family members have all died from brain haemorrhages, I'm not sure what she was thinking when I had my SAH, although it wouldn't be a stretch of the imagination to think that her sister and family were on her mind. Mum is more robust than steel. I find it incredible how she copes in adversity. She lost her dad and a younger brother prematurely as well. So unfair yet, I am a firm believer that mum is stronger having had to deal with losing such close family members while she was still so young herself. My rock, mum is always ready to pick up the pieces in a crisis. Always looking on the positive side, mum's glass is always half full although she could be forgiven for reacting half empty at times. Born with the strength of character to survive no matter what, mum readily takes on the family's troubles and strives to resolve any issues to the best of her capability. Granny depended on mum towards her later few months of life. As independent as granny liked to be, she had to admit defeat on occasions and ask for the help that she so desperately needed. Granny despised being needy. All her life she had fought for survival, looking after her siblings and having a significant role in running the crofting family household on the island. Doing as much for her family, as she was able, granny never looked for anything in return. However, when her health failed her so rapidly throughout 2005, it was mum she turned to for help. Mum, along with dad would visit granny daily, making the 35 mile round trip to the care home where granny spent her final months. It may have been shopping for a few small items but granny appreciated mum's help. No longer able to go out in the car herself, granny relied on mum. They enjoyed and valued each other's company. Even while ensconced in the care home granny could fill any void in conversation with ease, delighting with yet another tale from the old days. Mum too has many of granny's attributes and has a natural aim and ability to please. Mother, daughter? You would think. But no, mother-in-law, daughter-in-law.

Alison, first to show up in Ward 40, I think, for a visit. My memory, a bit blurred on some matters. Exceptionally rare, Alison is so reliable.

Visits every day, twice, sometimes three. With a vibrant personality and sensitivity to match, I was in good hands. Thoughtful and generous with her time, Alison easily anticipated the right length of visit. Like one of the family, I needed her there. That awareness to recognise how long to stay. Alert to my energy levels, I'm sure Alison was also a great source of comfort to my family. Chatted with ease, she was equally at home sitting in silence. The effect of just being there, the best. I would dose off when there were visitors. No point in fighting the exhaustion. Came with the territory of SAH. Just as well, complete bed rest, they said, compulsory until after surgery. And then, not pushing myself, short walks initially, I let my brain rest and recover. Opening up about my fatigue helped to keep stress levels at bay. Work commitments back home, delegated to others, supportive employer giving me the time to regain energy and concentration, I was afforded the time to recover. No needing to rush back to work too soon. Luck was on my side again, thank you Marcus.

Plant ecologist by day, Alison is an avid fiddle player in her spare time. With a high pressure career taking her to far flung places, alongside supervising PhD students from time to time, making space for music was precious and little. Short course enthusiast, Alison and I bonded over our music, first meeting in 1994 when I enrolled at university. I joined Alison's ceilidh band, The Gathering. That was the same band as I played in with Anne. Practices were held weekly, Alison's city centre flat. Cups of tea and chats the priority, we had to concentrate hard to make sure the music rehearsals were fitted in. Work hard, play hard, Alison is a high achiever. Decorated for her professional achievements at The Hutton Institute, Alison is more confident letting others take the lead when it comes to music. Personal development important and fun an absolute must, Alison stretches herself on fiddle, not to mention all the other instruments she plays, as well as singing. An active mind and nimble fingers, will no doubt have its benefits later in life too. Everyone could benefit from an Alison in their lives, this Alison.

2004, Spanish holiday. Alison and I set off on a week-long trip to the south coast. Keen student of the Spanish language, Alison grabbed every opportunity to use it. Combining relaxation at La Manga resort with rigorous exercise, mountain biking and hotel gym, we earned some R&R. Spa treatments, massages, warm jacuzzi baths and steam room sessions, mornings were spent researching Scottish music for an upcoming festival performance we were to give, on our return. Vacation over all too soon, it was time to return to the damp north of Scotland. Both Leos, Alison and I were similar in taste. Exercise, relaxation, good food! Ok, maybe those are not Leo traits, but the two of us were similar. We enjoyed swapping clothes. TBH, some of mine looked better on her, fitted Alison better. We had a similar sweet tooth.

October 2005, and a different kind of holiday. Cape Breton Island, Nova Scotia in Canada. Both fans of Cape Breton fiddle music, Alison and I hoped to meet and hear some of our all-time favourites; Buddy MacMaster, Jerry Holland, J.P. Cormier, Howie MacDonald et al. Flights organised by Alison, I booked the concert tickets. Sore neck on the flight, nothing that couldn't be sorted by a fix of Cape Breton fiddle on arrival, I thought. Anyway, after we landed in Halifax, Nova Scotia and a 4-hour drive in torrential rain and darkness, we landed at our accommodation in Cape Breton. Settled in at our log cabin, excited for what the week ahead would bring, the mucky weather on the journey had been worth it. No shortage of forests on the island, a few clearings giving rise to a town here and a village there. With hired car to enable us to get to gigs, we were keen to explore every nook and cranny of the island. Just like the Scottish Highlands, Cape Breton has a web of winding narrow roads at times. The coastal route of the island's Cabot trail, a mix of weathered shoreline and steep climbs. Views breath taking, Western Atlantic sea on one side, pine trees, spruce, fir and beech trees, the other, Alison and I, as fascinated to meet the people as we were to see the island. Feeling right at home, mixing with the locals, many of them of Scottish descent following mass emigration of the late 1700s, early 1800s, we turned night into day, attending the festival club after concerts, soaking up the music, time was short. Accommodation hosts on our side, we breakfasted daily at about 5pm, before setting off in the evenings to festival gigs. Renowned for an energetic and rhythmic style of fiddle playing, Cape Breton piano and hard-shoe stepdance, had us hooked too. Could have stayed forever. Flights booked, our time was up. Something like 17th October, 2005. 3 days until the brain bleed.

Afforded the opportunity to be open with my feelings, my close friends listened. And, listened. Without judgement or comment, concerned friends let me talk about my Middle Cerebral Artery Aneurysm (MCAA). Striking a balance was so important. Trying not to be narcissistic, I followed another tip from my psychology studying days, don't talk about yourself all the time. I encouraged family and friends to talk about themselves too, didn't I? I hope I did. MCAA clip my new friend, old friends all around me. Strength of support surrounding me and my family. Great friends, supporting me in my hour of need. Fragile, thankful, lucky. Grateful for their unwavering comfort, always. Will never forget it. 186 get well cards of support, to remind me.

Regaining Strength

Get up get strong again, where was my fighting spirit? It was going to take a bit of time. My two weeks of total bed rest had taken its toll. I had grown attached to the ward, almost happy to let the days drift by. The pace of life, slowed down while I waited, we waited. While I hadn't had a blow to the head, my body strength said otherwise. Overwhelmed, I was shocked at how weak I was after just 2 weeks in hospital. Weight plummeted by 14kg, I told myself, enjoy it while it lasts, the weight loss. Fully expecting the weight to go back on, my plan, do whatever it took to slow the process down. Keen to regain strength and get back to previous fitness levels, I set about going for short walks. Overwhelmed by exhaustion, I expected to bounce back to full fitness in no time. It was the Scottish Highlands, and November, after all. Swallowed up by the cold and a dose of fatigue along with it, I almost collapsed on my first venture outdoors. I'd persuaded mum to walk with me. Ended up limping to a neighbour's house and was thankful they taxied us back home. That's too strenuous, uttered dad. Lesson learned, I paced myself from then on, no pressure to rush back to fitness. Temptation all around, the kitchen cupboards bursting at the seams with all kinds of comfort foods, I had to try hard to remain in control of my diet. Didn't want to risk returning to 64kg in a hurry. I was vertically challenged, at only 5 feet 3 inches, and had a sweet tooth, very.

Alness, the perfect central base for a diligent, ambitious musician; journeys East, West and South reduced by two hours in each direction. A better place to live than my native Caithness, even though home comprised a picturesque, barren, rugged and remote setting. Quaint, unspoiled, not to mention, views to die for. Averon Leisure Centre, Alness had been my salvation. An abundance of young, fit and healthy, highly motivating staff, they encouraged all ages, no matter the fitness level, to engage in a broad range of activities. My preferred classes; Body pump and Kick Aerobics, the group leaders driving and pushing, persuading and supporting us to lift heavier weights, kick higher and to hop, spring and jump further. David and Rachel, our leaders, lean and hard, the goal for us all to strive towards. Later, synchronised Body Combat and Body Attack were introduced. Both classes popular and a full complement of participants twice weekly, Body Combat focused on precise techniques while Body Attack on high impact aerobics. I'd memorised the Kick Aerobics routine. Dad stressed about that too. Careful not to raise my heart rate too much, I tried to obey him. I compromised by missing out sit ups, at least for a couple of months. Averon, the place where, in the early 70s I'd won my first gold medal for Highland dancing.

Recuperation in Caithness with various family members had been a treat. Recovery behind me, physical that is, I had to face up to reality, reluctantly. I returned to Alness. Back on my own again, physically ok, but. The thought of being back there alone filled me with dread. I panicked at night when I went to bed, scared to go to sleep. I'd been spoiled. So grateful, the feelings of anxiety, subsided a little, over time. Personal Fitness Trainer, David Buchanan, fitness class trainer at the Averon obliged by setting up a programme in the gym for me. I could work out at a pace I was comfortable with after being away from it for so long. True to form, David proceeded to devise a highly ambitious fitness schedule. However, it was based on using equipment I felt comfortable with; no resistance machines, no weight lifting and no jogging on treadmills. Previously a hard task master, David was willing to devise a programme I felt safe doing but that also provided the flexibility to enable me to progress when I felt able to. One time fanatic of Body pump, Body Attack, Kick Aerobics and Body Combat, I had, ironically begun enjoying the self-directed pace of the gym. My level, my pace. Body Combat instructor, sick, and me too scared to return to body pump, I stuck to gym fitness. My subsequent workout meant I could exercise, when I wanted, at my pace, for however long I was able. Between 7 and 10am, four times a week, my initial preference, evenings and weekends reserved for relaxation and outdoor activities.

A twice weekly class, I used to love body pump. Never late, but not first to arrive either, I would always hope to sneak in to the back of the hall, inconspicuously. No such luck. Last to arrive inevitably ended up in the front row. There I was, the night of the brain bleed, front row, 30 others behind me. 'It' happened during the warm up. As I write, the visualisation of that night, and of body pump, brings back feelings of dread. Describing the routine, the gradual increase of weight on the bar, setting new lifting targets, and I am almost breathless. At times, at the gym, when there to do a workout, I would catch sight of the hall for the body pump class being set up, same painful emotion. How could I shake it off? The goal of the class, for me had been; gain some muscle definition, no bulking up. No expectation to have a full load of weights onboard. I would love to return to the class, but I know I won't. Stubborn, clouds of doubt, clutter my mind. Would it be safe to pump iron? I don't think so. The coldness and clamminess of my skin, unwelcome. Concern never shifting. Sensing another hostile eruption would occur in my head, it would be careless to return. Lifting heavy weights would be asking for trouble. Tempting another brain bleed is not on the cards. Best to be selective when it comes to risk taking. Try it, no? Enter the hall when the class is being set up? Participants yet to arrive? Can't be that worrying? Progress to touching the weight bar, feel the metal in my hand. Never again. Can't do it.

Thriving on exercise in the morning, it sets me up for the day. Better in control of my diet. Less likely to succumb to the temptation of bad food. Daytime felt safer. Being surrounded by people in the day, was a support. Night-times, alone, were more of a struggle. Time to think, time to worry. Ruminating about SAH would find its way into a negative place. Worry would spiral at times. Breaking the cycle, a challenge. Could I feel the clip inside my skull? Could I feel it move? What's that sensation, I would fear? What did it mean? When I didn't talk about my worries, I was silently thinking about them, anyway. Not good. Usual, upbeat attitude abandoned like an old rag. But, it wasn't a conscious decision. Didn't like the new me. If only I could see a glimpse of my old self. Even a shy light of hope would be promising. Bit by bit, my confidence would come back. There had to be light at the end of the tunnel.

The fresh air of the Cairngorm mountains and Rothiemurchas estate became my mood enhancer. Gone was the clutter of confusion that had occupied my mind. Time to put a stop to wallowing in self pity. Physically repaired, I cycled up Cairngorm mountain, chemistry restored. Exhilarated by the bond I felt with the manageable climb, it was July 2007. At 1079ft above sea level, cycling Cairngorm was a steady and steep incline No respite until you reach the top. Heart pounding, I considered turning back. How many times? Quite a few, I remember. The feeling of euphoria, achievement of reaching the top was fantastic. Reward, all around for miles, superb vista. The treat at the summit, a great long free wheel ride back down the mountain. Two days later, I would tackle the mountain cycle again. Faint drizzle initially, became a gradual heavy downpour. The steeper the gradient, the denser the fog, until I'd reached the summit. Had the damp air weighed down heavily on the mountain? A slower climb, all shades of mirky grey, somehow the task of reaching the top seemed much harder. It was July. It wasn't cold. Serenity all around, the road virtually deserted, peaceful, therapeutic, save for the mountain bus and a few cars. The route, off road at times, hardcore tracks with granite boulders. Had they been strategically placed to deter mountain bikers or grind them to a halt, almost? Great slabs of salmony grey, the rocks hung from the mountainside. Lichen and heather, speckled growth on the ancient rocks camouflaged their starkness. Pine trees and yellow broom, beautifying the mountain, soft blankets of moss and fluorescent ferns leaping out from behind a miriage of native greens. The sprinkling of native bushes added texture and colour to the otherwise monochrome vista. Mountain spring water gushed, bouncing in all directions, ricocheting off ancient boulders, cascading at speed down the mountain. My busy, outdoor break, therapeutic. The torment of the brain bleed lay dormant.

The London Effect

I don't mean to judge, or to draw conclusion. It's just, what I observed, growing up. Appreciated the discipline? Yes, It was good for us. A well-balanced upbringing, we enjoyed homemade, cooked meals at the family dinner table every night, not to mention, clothing courtesy of mum's amazing, creative, knitting and sewing capabilities. Most of the village kids would line up with requests for mum; gypsy skirts, ra-ra, Fair Isle & Icelandic jumpers, whatever the fashion at the time. Just like granny had been, mum is a giver. Home-bakes, beautifully made and decorated weekly, our house was popular after school. I remember others snacking on dog biscuits or fresh coconut, no lie, while we (Pauline, Douglas and myself) enjoyed home-baked Victoria sponges, rock cakes and bunnies (Queen cakes). Wish I had paid more attention to mum's talents. Knit? Yes. Follow patterns? No. Can manage a simple plain and purl stitch, a scarf at a push. Pull yourself together. Was that the message I heard? I think that was the family motto. We had a strict upbringing, yes, character-building. Would admitting fragility be a sign of weakness? No professional intervention by a counsellor when it came to emotional issues. The norm, I think, for the majority of Highland families. Secreting of personal anxiety demonstrated strength of character. Family illnesses and bereavement contemplated quietly, privately, behind closed doors, we developed our own coping mechanisms, unspoken ones. In our (siblings) formative years, mum protected us from anguish, too young to encounter the pain of grief, as a result of a family member or friend passing away. If only mum and dad had shared such burdens. A problem shared is a problem halved, don't they say? You might think, we took an ostrich approach, burying our heads in the sand, an out of sight, out of mind mentality. We were protected, sheltered. Bolster ourselves, quietly courageous, our coping strategy. I think I would have felt ashamed to admit I needed help for anything emotional, as a youngster. Dignity maintained, we felt robust. Personality, morals, judgements and coping mechanisms, set by previous generations, our Highland ancestors. There were very many positives. I hope I don't offend. I absolutely don't mean to.

Open up. Express the anxiety. Admit I had challenges. The brain injury seemed to bring out a different side to my personality. The morphine at work again. Unable to sweep my concerns under the carpet, the drugs enabled free expression. The first step on the road to recovery from the head trauma was to talk. No more looking at past generations, no stiff upper lip. I had to let it out. The privacy of our upbringing bred a reticence to express emotion, my reserved nature, exacerbated. Still working on it. As long as I played the fiddle, the instrument served as my voice. The handmade Maggini fiddle had spoken for me, exposing my innermost feelings.

In Ward 40, I felt free to express my worries. I needed to. No bottling up. Waiting all weekend for the cerebral angiogram, I felt especially tense. Worried, might time run out before it was too late? Do something, help me. The delay in getting treatment was a concern. Could I be saved? I opened up to the doctors, to my friends and family. No time for family motto. Had to let out the emotion I felt. Again, although on morphine, I was able to express the worry, it was calmly. Everyone was anxious, not just me. With scheduled days for various procedures in ARI, Monday was angiogram day. I waited, we waited. It seemed a really long time. Risks associated with the angiogram brought more anxiety. Desperate to have it. Scared to go through with it. Angiogram behind me successfully, lucky no allergic reaction to the contrast solution (iodine), the waiting began again. Wednesdays were surgical clipping days. After a further 48 hours, stabilised by morphine, no side effects from the angiogram, I was prepared for the open surgery on my brain. Anxiety levels under control from the morphine, I gave in to the next hurdle in my way, surgery. The day I had longed for had finally arrived. I would only begin to feel safe, once I'd come out the other side. I don't think I fully appreciated the enormity and risk involved, thank you, morphine. I had a deep sense of awareness for needing the operation. I believe this logic and clarity within me overrode the acute anxiety being felt by my parents and sisters who were there with me. Of course, they managed very well to save me from witnessing their fears which I am sure on reflection included worries of a possibly frightening outcome. Option? There was just the one. Had to take it. Crossed my fingers, closed my eyes. Thanks mum. Just goes to show, no matter how old you are, you are still your mother's daughter. I needed her there. I didn't ask. Mum showed up. Alone, in the corridor. Me, wanting to be by her side, she wishing I wasn't going into surgery. The best. Must have been a long day for mum. Always a knitter. I guess she took a break, that day.

Surgery of the nature I was undergoing, the law states, you must surrender your driving license. DVLA are not made aware of the surgery by the NHS. The onus is on the patient to admit. Driver's license automatically revoked. Eight months and two medical questionnaires later, plus field vision eye test, I was free to drive again. Complimentary public transport for the duration of the ban, would have been nice to be informed when I was able to take advantage, not after I had my licence back. My preferred mode of transport for journeys north, the train anyway. Proud to say though, when I do drive, I have set my own national speed limit of 50mph. Safer on the road and as an added bonus, the miles per gallon steadily go up. Statistically, as a female, I am less likely to be involved in an RTA. Reduced hours at work, initially, walking to work the norm, until my driver's license was reinstated. At first, I was spending as much time in work, as I was, walking there and back. I enjoyed the traffic free route that ran parallel to the babbling, Alness River.

Risk of epilepsy is increased in patients of SAH, reducing over time, where no seizure has occurred. Within two years of the initial SAH, risk of epilepsy returns to the same as for general members of the public.

That was good news. With no seizure, during, around or after my brain haemorrhage, I should feel confident I am back to low risk. Niggles in the back of my mind come on if I am swimming, particularly, deep water swimming. Gives me the creeps that I might fit. This concern is especially intense every time I swim in the deep end.

Needed a counsellor. Sympathetic, locum GP made an immediate referral. How was a neurologist going to deal with ruminations of rebleed and further aneurysm anxiety? That was, if another aneurysm hadn't already started growing? Managing to stretch the appointment out to twenty five minutes, ultimately it didn't feel like a valuable experience. So many unanswered questions. Solution said the neurologist, anti-depressants. I declined. I didn't trust that anti-depressants were the fix. I didn't agree in anti-depressants trying to make me believe I was safe. To me, they were trickery. Gut feeling, couldn't take them. No disrespect to others. I simply wasn't comfortable going there.

Locum GP visit repeated. Alternative solution needed. My neurosurgeon was suggested. Feelings of guilt took hold. Taking an appointment, when I had already been assigned my one allocated outpatient meeting. Not wanting to pester, might Mr Currie think my anxieties were bordering on trivial? Wasn't ready for him to behave as though my questions were insignificant. They were significant to me. Desperately grateful for the opportunity to speak to the only person I really trusted in disclosing my worries to, and, my dad, a close second, back I went, armed with list of woes. Needs catered for, calmly, with no impression I was a nuisance, fears abated once more. In the short weeks and months since leaving hospital I regularly panicked and was anxious about a range of concerns. I kept detailed lists of these anxieties so that I could go through my issues, hopefully with Mr Currie ensuring nothing would be left out that would come back to haunt me at a later stage. I can't praise Mr Currie highly enough for taking my exhaustive list and going through each concern one by one: the reassuring voice of the dedicated humanist and professional freely demonstrating his knowledge in laymen's terms. My worries ranged from concern that the clip might dislodge due to sneezing or coughing, that I could actually feel the clip moving due to either pains or sensations on the right side of my head, to worrying that my skull might be infected as one of the many books I have on medical conditions discusses infection after skull fracture: the lists go on. Why would the benefits I felt from seeing my surgeon and having the opportunities to reveal my worries become diluted in time when I am no longer around him to seek reassurance? I might have been considered an illness phobic. But no. Had I been phoning the doctors on hundreds of occasions making appointments, that would have been another matter. Really, really struggling to believe I was safe, researching like crazy to find somewhere, the words, that what had happened on the 20th, was going to happen again. To see it in print, would have been shattering. It's over. I do know. The vigilant me reads it could happen again. That's the bit that niggles. I no longer push the experts to confirm my fears. I am acutely aware of this perspective and make every effort to try and cope on my own. Inevitably those closest to me bear the brunt of the anguish I try to cope with. I subject my friends and family to my thoughts and feelings as seldom as possible. I try as much as possible to tolerate the discomfort of my worries without dragging everyone around me, down with me. Much praise for the temporary Thurso GPs in Thurso. Why then the turmoil rearing its ugly head on my return to Alness, six months later? Mis-information in Alness prevented progress, temporarily. No such thing as neuro psychologist in the Highlands, said one. No point in being referred, said another. The wait would be lengthy, years not months.

Bang, smack in the middle of trying to cope after the brain haemorrhage, came relationship breakdown. I found myself running away to London. With NHS referral to support my anxiety non-existent, cue, eminent psychiatrist Dr. Raj Persaud, Harley Street based. At my own expense, away I went for five, I think, hours of insight. Good decision. Alert to my predicament, Raj quickly formulated a succinct opinion of my crisis. Hooked on his approach, words of wisdom, support and acknowledgement of needs, I felt, whatever he was saying, helped. My dad, meanwhile, thought otherwise. Get yourself home, he said. He could fix the issues. Dad's confidence, admirable, but I was determined. Maybe more like him than I'd realised. Sticking with my planned, Raj appointments, I stayed in London until the end of the week. With Raj's endorsement that NHS Highland prioritise me for neuro psychology, waiting list no more! Yes, thanks to Raj, within a couple of weeks, I had my first NHS Highland neuro psychology appointment. Of course, during the 5 hours with Raj, it was inevitable we would touch on other subjects. Always within the context of the brain injury, the conclusion, I wasn't the only one in the relationship (romantic) who needed therapy. Anyway, that's another book! With his first degree in psychology and his second in medicine, I decided, Raj's intervention was the professional combination I needed. He is, however, more famed for his degree in Psychiatry. Personality captivating, and books to match, Raj, like my neurosurgeon, had the ability to keep my anxiety in check. At least, for the duration of the appointments, until I was assigned to neuro psychologist, Louise, at NHS Highland. In addition to neurosurgery Aberdeen, Raj had been my saviour. His presence had me gripped. Charming, bright, lively, upbeat, positive, young, exuberant, caring, astute, pin-pointing, on the button, engaging, drew me in.

So, published now, anxiety must be behind me? Turmoil of brain injury unravelled, subsided? Undecided, I think, coping with the anxiety rather than overcome it. Might it always be a work in progress? Think so. I decided early on that I didn't mind having the SAH, if it meant that someone else was spared from the same. While I coped well with the physical aspect of the haemorrhage, I hope the subsequent, emotional rot vanishes to reveal a forward thinking and positive outlook in all aspects of my life.

Not long into my history with Raj about my relationship breakup, the topic turned to brain injury. Disillusionment with my neurology appointment. In agreement that the only satisfaction I felt about my brain injury worries was alleviated by my surgeon, unfortunately, Mr Currie couldn't always be there. Resulting in only transient relief, the benefits of discussing my concerns with my surgeon so easily diluted within days and weeks of seeing him. If I was on the outside, today, looking in, what would be my thoughts? Section that person! Get them to a designated place of safety. Anxiety would re-emerge so soon after being allayed by Mr Currie. Louise said it was PTSD, post-traumatic stress disorder. Often on edge, uptight, early nights didn't make for a restful night's sleep. Rest is as good as sleep, no? Why do I encourage, reliving the brain haemorrhage? Would it not be less harmful to settle for spontaneous flashbacks in general? I do, and at the same time, I don't, want to relive 'the' experience in my mind. Why the comfort in reliving the experience? And, in contrast, why the fear to witness the body pump class? Lifting weights, a no no? On edge when I overheard participants chat about the class, no. Can't hear that. Better find a new class. Body pump class would be due to start, I would avoid being in or near the building. Feeling of guilt for chickening out, justified, right? Too late, sometimes, forgot the class was on. Pang of nerves. Where to hide? Peripheral vision would catch sight of the weights and the weight bars. I would try and look away. I would sometimes catch my subconscious, visualising me back at the class, and the consequences of doing that. I would feel my hands go clammy, sweaty and heart rate increase. All is good now. These days I have membership of another gym. There's no body pump there, phew! In attempting to overcome the fear I needed to address it. I needed to challenge the fear, head-on. Eventually I learned to feel comfortable picking up just a small weight. As I write this and put down my thoughts my gut instinct is that I don't want to get comfortable touching and handling heavier weights, say, 7kg and above. At the moment I feel on edge just writing about it, as writing about it means thinking about it and imagining going through with all these aforementioned ideas.

As the dark clouds lingered, I struggled with the emotional effect the illness had on me. I had seen myself as fiercely independent...until now. You'll get over it dismissed one GP. There's no such thing as a neuro psychologist in the Highlands he went on. His colleague intimated You'll have to wait two years for an appointment, I'm not referring you, there's no point. I didn't mind him not referring me. I went home and wrote my own referral. Thanks to Raj Persaud's intervention the total wait was about eight months.

Raj has an unbelievable wit and charm alongside an odd sense of taste in socks. I was incredibly struck by how quickly he understood my painful story and promptly offered some much needed and welcome advice. At the same time he carefully encouraged me to determine how to progress with my situation in a positive way. Raj was somewhat of a saviour to me. I would say that I am still attempting to deal with my turmoil. I am more comfortable with the insecurities I have. I want and need to feel it in order to never let go of the fact that I am changed.

I believe it is important not to rush into making decisions. I didn't believe I was rushing into changing career. I didn't feel the music for many days, weeks and months. I figured that was long enough to decide that the new me needed to divert from my music life. Maybe it's too soon to know whether I changed career too soon. In parallel to the turmoil I faced regarding my work, there is the neuro psychology. For months I desperately felt that I needed the counselling. Now that I am finally receiving the support, I question whether I do need it. I didn't cope well without it. Am I coping with it? I don't know. I found myself opposite Dr. Raj Persaud. He asked why I contacted him. His email was in my inbox from a year ago when I asked him about support after a SAH. It was a gut feeling in my relationship crisis that prompted me to approach him. I think everyone should see him. I have been tempted to go back. I was drawn to the Edinburgh Book Festival in August, five months after meeting Raj. After his appearance on stage at the festival Raj invited members of the audience to meet with him for a book-signing. I made sure I was first in the queue; to ensure that I would get the chance to speak to him, but also as my train out of Edinburgh was due to leave soon after. There was no time to waste. Raj was just the way I had remembered him, warm and interested. He immediately remembered my visit to meet him in London and quickly launched into wanting an update on my situation. It was definitely worth the long train journey from Aberdeen via Inverness to Edinburgh and back to steal a few seconds with Raj for a catch up. I left, thankful he didn't bill me for the time.

Full Circle

2008, Belford Hospital, Fort William. Time to demonstrate coping mechanism and give something back. No longer comfortable to be a taker of the support group, Headway Highland, I offered to help raise awareness for the setup of a new branch of the charity. In keeping busy and being an active supporter/volunteer for the organisation, I spent 4 days, armed with leaflets, posters and information about Headway. Engaging with staff, patients and visitors in the hospital, I spread the word about the charity and shared plans to set up a group locally. A positive experience, it marked a turning point in my emotional recovery. In his book, *The Motivated Mind,* Dr. Raj Persaud discusses the benefits and satisfaction of volunteering. I had come out the other side, transited the dark tunnel of fixation on brain doom. Emerging into the light, I was able to offer support and personal experience insight to prospective members of a new Headway Fort William group. On another occasion, I set up a stall at a country show. Selling merchandise and again, by way of postering and leaflet distribution, I was able to raise awareness of the charity Headway, in Caithness, where a new support group was also due to be established.

Wow, I mean, it wasn't in the plan, not at all, wanting to play fiddle again. I think initially, I didn't. I felt obligated to play at times. For 2 or 3 years, my good friend, Anne had tried to persuade me to play fiddle again. I was adamant, no! She thought I might enjoy it if I played fiddle again. I enjoyed not playing! Anyway, I had no fiddle. And then, she asked again, and I said 'okay' to the invite. I borrowed a fiddle. Thank you, Wendy. A few persuasions later and I began to feel a sense of discomfort at borrowing a fiddle. Wendy wasn't playing it, but somehow it didn't sit well with me, to ask too often for a loan of her fiddle. It was Wendy's fiddle, after all, not mine.

After selling my previous fiddle, some years before, I set about trying to find a modest replacement fiddle to buy. I didn't have to look far. Coincidentally, there were a few fiddles in 'The Reel', music shop in Kirkwall, The Orkney Islands, where I was just about to go on holiday. I explored options. Within a few days, after borrowing the front runner, I found myself buying an instrument that was in the shop on consignment, from a local islander. It's now 6 years later. I don't remember if I loved playing again immediately. Or, was it a case of, with the fiddle in my hands, playing and practising was more convenient? No need to continue borrowing and returning Wendy's fiddle to her. I wanted to love this fiddle. I had loved my previous one. I enjoyed the story that came with the new fiddle. It had been handed down through the generations in a local Orcadian family. From what I can remember, nobody in that family played the fiddle. The connection that the fiddle had with Orkney, I found interesting.

As a teenager, I had spent most days practising fiddle by looking out of my north-facing bedroom window, to the Orkney Islands, from mainland Caithness, where we lived. I had always found it inspiring to practice that way, mesmerising almost. Close enough at our house, with the window open, I could smell the sea, hear the waves. The inspiration didn't come much better than that. I didn't need encouragement to practice when I was a teenager. I was keen to improve. The hours would fly by, when I used to practice in my teens. A very rural and remote area, there was little else to stimulate and encourage a teenager in John O'Groats. More than satisfied, I thrived on the fresh air and lack of commercial temptation. So, with new fiddle in hand, I remember sometimes, wishing I had my old fiddle back. Still unsure how much or little I wanted to play again, I was just a little curious about my old Maggini fiddle copy. But, I couldn't afford to buy it back. I had to get over any notion of missing the old fiddle and begin the task of practicing and re-learning my old repertoire of tunes again. I was rusty, yes, that's for sure, but brushing up on my old skills and techniques didn't take too long. Anne and I loved playing dance music together. I had grown up, listening to so many Scottish Dance bands, accordionists, fiddlers and pipers at home and at family ceilidhs. The tunes weren't far away. Some were tucked away in a corner or 2 of my brain. I spent a bit of time polishing my playing. Practising with Anne made all the difference. Anne's rhythmic keyboard playing served to enhance my quality of playing. Although born a Geordie, the music didn't come any more Scottish than Anne's playing. A versatile musician and core member of many bands and groups over the years, I loved to spend time with Anne, practising sets for a ceilidh dance or concert. The lift and groove in Anne's keyboard playing spurred on the quality of my own playing. We bounced off one another, playing reel after reel, strathspey after strathspey, jig after jig.

In 2019, I secured some funding from Aberdeen City Council for Anne and I to deliver live music performances in nursing homes and care homes in and around Aberdeen. My proposal had been to bring the ceilidh to the vulnerable in society. With elderly residents no longer fit to go out and about, Anne and I brought our music to them, 10 performances in 5 homes. The senior citizens loved the music. Many would clap along to Anne and my tunes. Others appeared to nod off, but we would notice they were tapping their feet in time to the music. Care staff also enjoyed the music. It was a rewarding experience for us all. The feedback was great. I was very grateful that the council recognised the value of bringing traditional music to the elderly. It was music therapy. Ironically for me, the therapy after my SAH was to abandon my music. I often used to think that Anne and I were only one generation away from being a potential resident ourselves. We could relate to the age group. We would talk about the music we were playing. The audiences would light up on recognising the tune and song titles, joining in with a chorus or two e.g. when we played, The Northern Lights of Old Aberdeen. For myself in particular, I was finding my way again, playing fiddle in public after so many years on a break after the haemorrhage.

These performances were intimate, with numbers of between 20 and 40 attending. This allowed Anne and I to play acoustically, without a PA system, speakers, monitors or microphones. Being on the floor, in front of our audiences, allowed me to walk around and approach our spectators. I was able to engage with our audiences more easily and interact with them. Some had vision problems, others were hearing impaired. I think they appreciated the interaction. From a practice point of view, nothing enhances your playing standard more than to perform to a live audience. The interaction between Anne and myself was clear for our audiences to see. Naturally very smiley, Anne brought the best out in me, so that I looked less serious than I normally would. Although, to this day, my biggest smiles tend to happen when I've made a mistake. I don't know, but I remember, when I was a lot younger, if I made a mistake while playing fiddle, I could never recover from it. Mind blank, my place in the music was lost. Audiences would be waiting. I would forget the tune, forget the key. Poor Anne would be left 'vamping' solo on keyboard, willing me to find the place in the music and join in with her again.

I wonder whether, if with maturity, comes a sense of calmness, that all will be okay. If I make a mistake nowadays, I can switch to another familiar tune, hopefully, usually. Or, if playing with another melody player, I can go silent momentarily and listen to the other player before more easily catching up. I think, trusting that the music sounds good helps with the recovery from making a mistake. It's always helpful if a mistake occurs in the middle of a set. Mistakes are less memorable to an audience if they don't happen at the end. Of course, if the majority of your audience are not musicians themselves, then they are even less likely to even notice errors in the first place, wherever they happen in a tune. When I teach, I usually say to my students, that if they play confidently enough, mistakes will sound intentional. It's my attempt to offer encouragement, to not be afraid of making a mistake. Thing is, though, if playing 'by ear' (from memory), when you make a mistake, it's really hard to not make the same mistake when repeating a measure of the tune. Your short-term memory can often send you to the same wrong note, next time around. When that happens, my advice, when practising, is to isolate the short phrase, around where the mistake was made, practice to correct the mistake and then replay the tune.

So, it was about two years after taking up my fiddle playing again, when I decided I would teach a fiddle workshop or two. It wasn't something I pursued initially. I was invited by a local community group to teach. It was an honour to be asked. Might it be instrumental mayhem? A part of me guessed that having had such a long gap since playing/teaching after my illness, that other, younger players would now be getting those teaching opportunities that I had once enjoyed. Pleasantly surprised and grateful for the opportunity to teach again, it was heartening to see some familiar as well as new faces at these workshops. And so my fiddle rose from the ashes. It certainly bolstered my confidence that players returned to my workshops. Until now, I didn't know if teaching fiddle was something I really wanted to do again. In the couple of short days taking that plunge again, I realised the positive results. Faced with the challenge of mixed ability fiddle players, my teaching techniques and tips seemed to come back to me quite quickly. Watching the class and listening to their competencies provided me with the content I needed to teach e.g. bowings, ornamentation (embellishments), dynamics and intonation (playing the notes correctly). One of the challenges with the fiddle is, there are no frets. The player needs to find the correct note using muscle memory. These were all aspects of their fiddle playing I could focus on helping them to improve. I think patience and a willingness to ensure the class progresses are vital when teaching. Patience in abundance, I loved recognising the gaps in students' skills and guiding them to overcome them. When I teach I believe, it's not vital that students achieve everything in one go. Learning a tune takes time. Learning the bowings, dynamics and ornamentations can challenge a fiddler. The important thing is that the player understands how to approach achieving the above, so that with continued practice and time, they can get there.

Active participation in lessons is vital to the learning process. An understanding of the instructions, enables learners to make use of the advice, and to apply the techniques, in their own time, at a speed that works for them. My role as a fiddle teacher, is to facilitate fiddlers in learning, without any fear that they are or might become a better player than me. I admire players who are better than me. But if I can demonstrate a style tip or technique associated with my own playing to another player, it's something I celebrate, without fear that they might be more proficient on the instrument than I am. My motto is that I am challenged technically on fiddle. When I say challenged, what I mean is that certain keys and positions on the fiddle are outwith my capability. However, what I am able to do, I do very well. I play well, I teach better. I also believe that I can improve my technical playing ability. That's going on my bucket list. When I teach, I point out that the techniques I share also apply to existing tunes in the repertoire of players. Future learning becomes easier as these same techniques are delivered in my classes, but by using new tunes. The reinforcement of the techniques enables learners to make progress. The focus of future workshops allows students to concentrate on learning new material while applying previously learned technique.

It was still prior to Covid-19 and I think I had taught just two full day workshops plus a couple of 1:1s. I had finally arrived, I think, at the realisation that I enjoyed playing and teaching again. While I still find playing fiddle quite challenging, I feel quite solid in my confidence as a fiddle teacher. It certainly feels really good to know that players have enjoyed my workshops and take the time to write or message and let me know. I am still working on re-learning the vast repertoire of tunes I used to play before my brain illness. When playing in music sessions, I find it hard to remember what tunes I used to play. When another player starts a tune, I will often find that I remember it from years before. I notice though that I often don't remember it as well as I used to. My playing quality of these tunes is less. I should go to more sessions and record them. I can then work on re-learning the tunes to a better standard, ready for future sessions.

During Covid-19, when I found myself furloughed from my day job, publishing a book of my own compositions became my mission. Reflecting on that idea, I sometimes wonder if it was a wise decision – to publish a book when all shops were closed. The target market for such a product is also quite small. The odds were not in my favour. Add to that, I decided to have 1100 books printed and that was a lot of bookshelf space I needed to find a home for. I had a built-in wardrobe constructed. I set about composing some tunes, to add to my existing repertoire of self-penned music. From initial idea to seeing my book in print took 28 days. I researched printing companies. I think I chose the best. I hunted online for advice on how to publish. I looked at existing music books for design ideas. I wrote an introduction for my book and biography. I approached prominent musicians in the traditional fiddle world and invited them to endorse my book. I obtained sample books in order to assess paper quality for the internal pages and book cover quality. The book would need to be able to stay open on a music stand. Taking ownership of the project was a must. Self-publishing meant I was in complete control of the book from start to finish.

My tune book was a huge personal achievement. How many people can say they have published a book? My advice would be, go for it. Get it on your bucket list. Do it! There are many ways to approach book publishing. Here I am again. This book has taken longer than 28 days to turn around. I think I started writing it in July 2007. I went through periods of thinking it wasn't good enough. I thought that it might be of no interest to people. At times I have wondered, would readers think that my writing style wasn't good enough? Well, if people only ever published a book when they thought it couldn't ever be written better, very little publishing if any, would ever get done. To write and to publish and then to think it could be better, suggests there might be a second book in there somewhere. For me, this book is how I feel. Now feels like the right time for me to deliver it. The beginning of this book is my personal experience of coping following SAH. I've read stories, some recently, in the press and on social media about others who have succumbed to a bleed on the brain. I want to think that those people didn't suffer. I want to believe that they weren't consciously in pain. From my own experience, my vivid memories are of simply not feeling quite right. From that feeling, I went to there being no doubt in my mind that something was worryingly not right with my head. But then there was calm, there was quiet and my breathing went shallow. My subconscious let it happen. By then I was feeling calmish, I think. I hope that readers will not fear knowing someone that this has happened to. I mean, I'm not advocating for burst aneurysms of course. Moreso, I'm reflecting on my experience. It was manageable. Woozy, dizzy, feeling weak, scared for what was to become, plus headache that only subsided when the morphine was administered. I am not, definitely not suggesting that it wasn't a bad thing. Keep safe. I want knowledge of my experience to be what others think it is like for anyone who has a SAH. If a loved one passes away as a result of a SAH, I want readers to imagine that person could have experienced the same as I did when I had my bleed. It was not a raging headache. It was not like a punishing migraine. It was a series of experiences quite unlike what you might imagine. Knowing that myself I think, helps me to cope with the feelings that if it were to happen again, I would try to cope the same way. The circumstances of another bleed might obviously be different e.g. bleed in a different part of the brain, somewhere deeper, perhaps inoperable. That might possibly come with a different set of experiences. My coping mechanism I think, is to imagine that if I handled it in the same way that my experience might be the same or that the outcome would be the same. That's my survival instinct. Yes! That for me is turning a corner! To truly believe and imagine that is how I might feel, react, if a future experience of similar was to occur.

I found my music life again, thanks to the encouragement and persuasion of my incredible friend and accompanist, Anne Taylor. It's immensely sad that Anne is now no longer with us, having succumbed to the cruelty that is cancer, on 28th June, 2022. Anne is missed hugely and had been a great friend to so many of us. Anne was very passionate and gave her all to knowing as much as possible about the subjects that meant the most to her. She will forever be remembered by me as a loyal friend, great musician and dance-caller. Anne was courageous and made time for people. How she managed to find that much time for so many of us, I don't know. I truly valued Anne's friendship and the time she made for me, as a friend and a musician. So many great memories. Rest easy my fellow cat lover, and amazing dear friend, thank you, Anne.

NUDGED...

Epilogue

What now? Composing, re-learning, practising teaching again. These aspects of fiddling have crept back into my life again. There's a passion in me to improvise and experiment with my music in a way that I didn't feel confident doing before. My self-esteem has been bolstered. When Covid came, I thought, how could I practice teaching? I set about making some contacts. One email and a zoom call later with Marcia in the USA I secured an online teaching opportunity. North West Scottish Fiddlers, Seattle hosted my workshop. A total of 53 fiddle players from all over the USA, including some from Scotland, logged onto the session. I gave it my best shot. We all had to adapt during Covid. It didn't take long to settle into the workshop. Lucky really, as the workshop itself was just 2 hours long. The time zone difference of 8 hours was a little challenging for me. Small consolation for the turnout, the enthusiasm and the great feedback. I came away feeling like my feet were back under the table. I felt like a fiddle teacher again. It was a virtual class I know but that's the biggest fiddle class I had ever taught.

I feel invigorated by the craft of writing music. The creative process and dedicating tunes to friends and family is my way of connecting, honestly with people. It's a compliment to the recipient. It's not a selfish thing. Practicing writing music helps me to improve the quality of my compositions. Practicing using the electronic software expands my skills and knowledge in the discipline of creating sheet music. I thrive on creating good works and sharing them with other musicians, clubs, friends and family. It doesn't matter when a recipient themselves doesn't play. The finished product, the written sheet music in PDF can be framed/displayed like any other gift. It's personal to that individual or group. You could consider that my focus on writing music itself is adding another string to my bow. The writing process often involving; repeated practice of an idea, accept or reject, consolidate and add to it. Sometimes the music will come to me holistically i.e. as an entire tune or in two separate parts. I use a combination of writing the composition down and recording on the voice recorder of my phone. The ideas are locked in. But they can easily be adapted, scrapped or end up being the finished tune. Ultimately, I am 'working' in music but in a different way to my former musical life. I feel capable, I have the confidence, I believe in what I do. And then at workshops I can teach, share, gift my tunes and the techniques that go with them. It's like a new beginning for me. Coming at it with some relative experience helps. Oh, my tune for Molly was just awarded 1st place at Banchory Music Festival, yesterday, Saturday 13th May 2023. Always nice to get a bit of recognition for effort.

Let's go back to the near beginning of my story. I mentioned organ donation. To explain my feeling comfortable with organ donation these days, realistically I would say that I am less uncomfortable with the idea. No longer creeped out, I almost jumped at the chance to go on the register after the SAH. I don't think I could be a direct living or altruistic (living, but without knowing the recipient) donor. But I experienced the sensation of losing consciousness, remember? What's my willingness to sign up for organ donation post mortem? For a while I had drifted around a state of semi-consciousness. It was gentle, quiet, soft, no fight or struggle. With no memory of unconsciousness, I tell myself, there's nothing to be afraid of. Willing to accept an organ if I need one, I should be willing to donate one when I pass. Experiencing the brain haemorrhage and the symptoms that came with it leads me to that conclusion. Decision made, card in my pocket. I have signed up, willing to donate all organs except the corneas. Can't do the eyes. Sorry, forgive me please. I feel proud. Organ donor card dated 31st May 2006. Yours? The rules have changed in The UK, no longer an 'opt-in' process in Scotland, England and Wales. It is assumed that most adults living in England and Wales are advocates of organ donation. In Scotland, the same applies to anyone age 16 and over. In all cases there are some exceptions. By the time this book has been published, N. Ireland will have adopted the opt-out scheme too, planned date, 1st June 2023. Hope this is not too morbid a subject for you to digest.

Remember the significant date of the main theme of my story? Brain haemorrhage, 20th October, 2005. Well, exactly 10 years to the day, in 2015, I found myself back in ARI. This time, I was having surgery for cancer. Skin graft rejected. More surgery? How so? Knee surgery this time, malignant melanoma. The most deadly form of skin cancer, I thought I would be dead before Christmas. Not an easy drive home from work after the telephone call I received that day from ARI. There had always been a blackish small mole on my knee. Born with it. My normal. It didn't ever bother me. If I didn't burn on the first few days of a beach holiday, I used to consider, it hadn't been good value for money. Tenerife 2014, daily morning bike ride. Cat lover. Had to go and visit the beach cats. Marco, my favourite. Back to the hotel, shower, breakfast, factor 10 suncream applied. It might have been factor 15. Certainly no higher protection than that. Bikini donned, sunbed time and a good read; Another Day in the Frontal Lobe, by neurosurgeon Katrina Firlik or Martin Kemp's autobiography, subject matter – brain tumours, when not reading a good bit of crime fiction. I don't know. There must have been something. Hide that with a plaster (Elastoplast), I told myself. The thing was, the cancer was in me. The knee was just where it decided to manifest itself. Hiding the black, yucky, nasty with a patch was never going to make it safe. Just a matter of time. The mole on my knee had started to grow a little, I thought. Edges ragged, texture raised, it seemed to have the hallmarks of something suspicious. With the mole covered up, I went back to enjoying the holiday. Hotel activities included French Boules. The prize for winning; a certificate and the cocktail of the day. Bagged a few certificates but always swapped the cocktail for prosecco. I met two ladies. Both widowed, one recently. Offering my condolences, the lady revealed her husband had died from skin cancer. All the excuse I needed to mention my knee, she had a look. Oh no, she said. It didn't look like skin cancer. Home from the holiday, concern in the back of my mind, something made me decide to have it checked out. GP confident I had nothing to worry about, I went away. At the time I felt ashamed. Had I wasted the doctor's time? Taken an appointment that someone who was actually sick might have needed? While my GP was unconcerned, the nurse at my work thought otherwise. I decided to trust the opinion of the GP. He was better qualified, wasn't he? It was another year before the mole began to itch. The only relief from the itching came when I would smack the area around the mole or scratch, but never the mole itself. Couldn't risk the mole bleeding. With the itch by then frequently happening, I made another GP appointment. Same GP, he hummed, saying it looked different to before. I don't believe he remembered the appointment the previous year. Anyway, after arranging an urgent referral to the dermatology department, ARI, the GP advised there would be an additional 6 weeks wait. With no cancellations, I had telephoned every day to check, the biopsy (removal of the mole) was carried out on 25th August 2015.

Six weeks I had to wait for the histology on the biopsy, the diagnosis. It was on 'the biggest coffee morning of the year', Friday 25th Sept. 2015 when I was told the mole was cancerous, malignant melanoma. The dermatology consultant had warned me previously, if it was melanoma, further surgery would be needed. The nightmare was still happening. WLE (Wide Local Excision) to remove more skin and flesh for testing, skin graft and lymph node removal were all recommended. Cancer in my right knee, smallish, black, irregular edge, just like the books describe. Raised surface, fragile, I was worried it would bleed when I knocked it. Date for skin removal in my diary, I'd been up a ladder a few days before, painting walls. The cold, right-angled metal steps, hard, but not sharp, I tried to focus on the paint and the brush. A couple of knocks, I panicked. Couldn't risk any cancerous cells spreading, at least not any more than they might already have. With cancerous cells also discovered in the good skin surrounding the mole, I had to undergo a WLE (Wide local excision). This would help to ensure that all cancerous cells were removed. Performed under local anaesthetic, I turned up at the hospital, crystal in hand for good luck. Once again I was treated with respect and dignity. Consultant plastic surgeon, Mr Depasquale (Maltese) performed the surgery. Same empathic nature as my neurosurgeon, exactly ten years previously, back in ARI, I felt like a VIP. The care and treatment there was, simply the best. Another highly skilled and experienced surgeon with exactly the supportive personality that gelled with me, I was in great hands. Mr Depasquale's nursing team, with empathy to match, I shouldn't have worried. Comfortable to lose mobility in the leg, I rejected a skin graft. Leg strapped rigidly in a brace from ankle to groin for a week, ensured no bend in the knee where the fresh stitches were. Research done, I refused the recommended sentinel node biopsy. The advised procedure involved the use of a nuclear solution in locating the sentinel node. The use of nuclear substances is becoming increasingly common in the diagnosis and treatment of health conditions and diseases. My morbidity in 2005 had prevented me from challenging the use of radioactive iodine. In hindsight, I wouldn't have rejected the angiogram procedure. It was a vital step in determining the course of action for the brain op. In 2015, I had time and clarity to research the sentinel node biopsy. It wasn't so much not wanting radioactive material in my body, I was more concerned for an incorrect diagnosis following the procedure. From what I understood, a specialist would examine the sample by looking through a microscope. I'd read about false positive diagnoses, where the person analysing the sample, believes they are looking at cancerous cells, when there are none present. Couldn't risk a radical sweeping out of all lymph nodes in my groin, in error. Decided I would take my chance, in the hope there was no cancer there. Paced myself again, regaining flexibility in my leg. There's a surprisingly generous amount of flesh around the knee. I was able to bend it again before long. The support received from plastics was second to none. Born to cry? No. Born to pick myself up and push forward. It did make me stronger, after a while. Like the SAH, if the melanoma were to return, I would be in stronger position to cope better. I would be more resilient, bounce back from the trauma. No follow up appointments this time? Yes, for 5 years, plus an additional year, due to covid. Regular visits to dermatology, thorough skin checks to assess for more potentially harmful moles. Invited to take part in a medical trial, I agreed to check my skin on a monthly basis, according to the directions on the Samsung Galaxy Tablet. Experimenting with the software, designed to log and report anything new or changing with my skin, I followed the process for the duration of the trial period. Feedback reported, the purpose of the software, to enable self-checking of skin between consultations with dermatology specialists. Quite straightforward to use, my only real comment was that I would benefit from the audio instructions being repeated, to ensure comprehension, but more-so my short-term memory, in being able to carry out the various checks. A great invention, to supplement healthcare provision I concluded.

It's been almost 18 years. Feels like yesterday. Grateful to share the journey in print, with your good selves. Thank you. I wonder what would go in your autobiography? If you have one, let me know. I would be interested to read. So what else has changed with my music? I find myself exploring the music my dad introduced me to. Long before I began to learn fiddle, at home we had Scottish dance bands on LP and cassette. I was a listener growing up. As a player, I glimpsed very briefly at dad's kind of music. Couldn't avoid it. When the family weren't listening to the recordings, dad would be playing it live, every lunchtime and every night. In his day job we lived close to work, the UKAEA site, Dounreay. In his allotted 39 minute lunch break, Dad would come home, strap on his box (accordion) and thrash out a few punchy strathspeys and rippling reels. Mum had prepared him a bite to eat. Dad would grab and go, back to his desk in the nick of time.

With the excitement and drive of Alasdair Fraser's playing in the mid 80s, my head had been turned. What was that sound he was creating? How did he do it? Could I learn to emulate Alasdair's playing? Not wanting to be a copycat, my goal was to get some punch in my jig rhythms, some sass in strathspeys, my reels to be as exhilarating as the sea crashing on rocks, and more. Most importantly though, to find my own fiddle voice. You've learned of my fascination for Cape Breton Island. In a way, it was like I had gone in search of something more exciting, different to the music I was raised listening to. I hadn't allowed time to fully explore the specific music of my upbringing. It's not that it didn't affect me, emotionally, I mean. More, I took it for granted. Didn't appreciate that it was special, almost. Somehow, like spoken accents and dialects. We think everyone else speaks with an accent except ourselves. I don't think I fully appreciated the dialect of Scottish dance music. Hindsight is a great thing. I would urge everyone to value their heritage and traditions. These days I find myself exploring the very sound that my dad incited me with as a youngster. I love to play along with accordion and piano. Not hesitant more, carefully tip toeing with the tradition, I value relearning the repertoire of my youth and combining it with instruments associated with the Scottish dance band scene. I would say, I am enjoying leaning towards that influence. Discovering some musicians who have a similar attitude to respecting the instrument combination has been cathartic. Strong, powerful, dynamic playing appeals to me. Exploring accordion, fiddle, piano and guitar in varying combinations has been inspiring. It feels good that there is a part of dad's music in my playing today. Definitely not a clone, I'm exploring my own voice while at the same time respecting my upbringing.

I wasn't predisposed to the anxiety. The PTSD brought on by the physical illness, got me for a while. I've been better equipped to deal with anxiety, because I wasn't born anxious. Never witnessed it around me. Good, solid, supportive, disciplined upbringing. Shaped, moulded, encouraged and guided through opportunities. Some blips along the way. Incredible network of family and friends to support me through life. Allow fear to eat away at you and I believe, some new illness will get you. Take care out there. Keep negativity at bay. Pick your times to care less. Try to avoid being careless. Have a great and productive life. Final tip, in the words of the late, Prime Minister of the United Kingdom, Sir Winston Churchill, *Success consists of going from failure to failure without loss of enthusiasm.*

Acknowledgements

Inside and out, I was blown away by all the cards, flowers, messages of care and visits from you all, during my hospital stay and beyond. It's taken me almost 18 years to thank every one of you for your well wishes and kind thoughts. Overwhelmed to receive 1, 2, 3 sometimes 4 or 5 letters and cards during my hospital stay and recovery, thank you all, from the bottom of my heart

Alison & Dougie

Alison & Peter

Anna

Niece Ashlyne

Niece Ash Bash, Nephews Kyle & Craig

Auntie Evelyn

Auntie Nan & Margaret

Betsy Lord

Bob Fraser

Brian & Irene MacLeod

Brian McNeill

Carley Williams

Carol-Anne Mackay

Caroline Reagh & Barry

Cathie & John

Niece Charlene

Cherry (Margaret) Clark

Christine & Eilidh Yorston

Colleen Gaudin

Darren

Dave & Linda Ross

Deirdre

Denise

Donal Brown

Dougie & Honda

Eilidh Steel & Mark Neal

Ellie Innes

Elspeth (London)

Eric & Tracey

Evelyn

Everyone at Dannsa

Fin Moore & Sarah Hoy

Fiona Cameron

Fiona Cuthill

Fiona Dalgetty

Garry & Jackie Dickson

Grant

Grant Sinclair

Hamish Moore

Hanneke Cassel

Hielan' Toe Dancers

Iain Fraser

Ishbel & Fred McBoyle

Jamie Laval

Jan Banis

Janet

Janice

Jenny Smith

Jimmy & Sandra Sinclair

John & Dot Cormack

John Sawkins & Aileen Paton

John Sikorski

Johnny Murphy

Karel Fialka

Karen Nic

Katherine Doversberger

Keith & Mary Scammell

Kitty Mason

Lachie Campbell

Libby Wilson

Liz (Barra)

Lizzie & Ken

Lynda Norburn & family

Margaret Sutherland

Marjorie & cello

Marrie Coghill

Mary

Maureen & Brian (Obsdale Gdns)

Mhairi Beaton

Mia Scott

Murdo Chambers

Nicola Hunter

Noel & Lily Mackay

Norma Brown & Ivor

Rachel Mennie

Rita Hunter

Rita Leavesley

Roz & Brian Bell

Ruaridh

Sally & David Body

Sally & Lily Caunt

Sandra Robertson

Sheila Urquhart

Sinclair Mackenzie

Sonia (Inverkeithing)

Stan Reeves

Susan & Frank Steel & Emma

Val Hewison

Ward & Sheila McCutcheon

Winnie

Addie Harper & family & fiddlers at Wick College: Ishbel Begg, Sheila
Main, Laura, Brian Polson, M Crosse, Madeline Mackay, Katy
Henderson, Della Wright, Irene Mackay, Katrine Macdonald,
Elizabeth MacLean

All at Wick RBLS Pipe Band
all of us at the Scots Fiddle Festival
Allan & Anna MacLeod, Alison, Neil & Peter
Ami & Graeme (Drama Dept. NHC)
Andrew MacIntosh & all the directors at ceòl beò
Ann & Albert Linklater & Eileen

Ann Ward & Norman Chalmers
bhuainn uile aig Sabhal Mòr Ostaig: Catherine, Sarah Naylor, Gabhan
Parsons, Elsie, Arline, Caoimhín

Nephews Craig & Kyle & Robbie Mackay
David & Helen Laing, Dianne & Joanna
David & Jennifer Broughton, Granville & Roger
Don & Karen Mackay & family
Elise Lyall & Martin Gill & Elise Lyall Highland Dancers
Ellen & Fraser Wilson (Clashmore)
everyone to do with Culture Ceol na Coigich: Midge, Marilyn, Evelyn,
Anne, Alistair

friends in Limerick: Mats, Brian, Sandra Joyce, Mick
George & Doris Farquhar & family
Isobel & Simon Grewcock & Murdo Farquhar
Jacqui MacDonald & George, Lindsay & Morven & Amber (woof)
Jed Mugford (Fiddle On Magazine)
Jo & Simon Harmer, Danny & Maria
John & Pippa Saunders, Finlay & Ellen
Joyce & Donald Gorman & Kirsty
Kevin & Erika Shearer, Nicol & Aaron
Cousins Kieran, Richard & Danny Dickson
Lily & Noel Mackay and family
Liza Mulholland & Bruce MacGregor
Sister Maree, niece Ashlyne, nephews Craig & Kyle
Cousin Margaret, Syd & Lewis Matheson
Mary Ann Kennedy & Nick Turner (Watercolour Studio)
Mats & Emma Melin, Solveig, Ingrid & Magnus
Niall (long lost cello) Laybourne
North Highland College, Alness staff: Les, Denise, Iris, Dru Pike, Diana,
Angie, Mary, Janice, Karen, Nic, Jamie (IT)

NHC Alness students: Campbell, Evelyn, Annie, Anne,
Cecil, Alex & Adam Sutherland, Jimmy MacEwan, Anna-marie, Kieran,

Carol, Alan, Chris, Faye, Peter, Rich, Catriona, Jamie, Rachael, Dana, Laura, Tommy, Al, Will, Keith

Cousin Pamela & Keith Wilson, Elizabeth Rose & Olivia
Sister Pauline, niece Charlene (& her friend Alison) & nephew Darren
Pete & Carola MacCallum & Solveig
Pete Honeyman & staff at Perth College UHI
Cousin Rosemarie MacQueen & James Clare
Sandra Robertson & Davie Douglas
Sara & Chris Bell & the girls
Sara & Helen @ Glasgow Fiddle Workshop
Seumas & Alison Grant (formerly of Dept of Celtic, Aberdeen)
Sheena & Alastair MacDonald, Michelle & Rhona
Sofie Jonsson & Andy Thorburn
Thurso/Dounreay Strathspey & Reel Society
Yvonne Turfus & Frank, Mattie & Jimmy Turfus

I was inspired to write the book to bring my personal experience to you. In doing so, I would like to take this opportunity to also salute my incredible family, NHS surgeon, caregivers and friends for being there for me, in my darkest hour. From the bottom of my heart, you have been amazing; mum, dad, sisters Pauline & Maree, brother Douglas, auntie Evelyn and cousin Helen, surgeon Mr David Currie, the doctors and nurses of NHS Highland and Grampian and friends Anne, Wendy, Alison and Pete as well as university lecturer Seumas Grant, uncle Dainie (not only for visiting on surgery day, but for finding and bringing Puddy north to be with the family while I recuperated), Ward, Sheila & Grant. Thanks so much auntie Evelyn and cousin Helen for making the journey down to Aberdeen and to Evelyn for the numerous letters and cards while I was in hospital. These are the names that spring to mind. Lachie – for checking in on Puddy and for mopping up her sick, after I fed her too many prawns, thank you. I forgot, how do you take your coffee? Is it black or white? And to friend Shirley for all the great recovery visits and card games in John O'Groats.

Marcus, North Highland College. Thank you for going above and beyond to allow me a full recovery before returning to work. I was humbled by the personal visits and phone calls of concern.

My family: mum, my incredible mum, who has faced so much heartache over the years and lost so many family members. How steadfast, strong and reliable you are, mum, thank you. Never an argument, always support. Incredible baker, cook, knitter, seamstress, dancer, supporter of all things heritage. Family is everything to mum. Mum is the glue that keeps us all together. Thank you for being there for me, mum. Knows when to talk, when to stop, how much to say, how little, calm, supporting, resilient. In the face of adversity, the world on her shoulders, mum dusts herself down and does her amazing thing. Dad. Well he was there, through the pain of losing his own mum, dad stayed with me. Must have had a lump or two in his throat, trying to keep it together for me, when he could so easily have fallen apart. I will never forget. Quieter than mum, but his presence was a magic wand. Dad's faith, strength and calmness, while all around him, the turmoil of sickness and granny's death.

Pete MacCallum, Neil Mathewson, Kathryn Preston, Dave @ The Digital Audio Company, Alasdair Fraser & Jerry Holland - for making the Ward 40 CD happen. Beautifully efficient, generous, professional and supportive.

Finally, last but not least a big thank you to Alastair. We have reconnected in recent years through music. Alastair has guided and supported my work along the way. His knowledge of music theory, musicianship, expertise in sound engineering, willingness to help and encourage the creative process has resulted in my being able to achieve goals to a much better standard.

Bibliography

Darke, K. (2006) *If You Fall…: It's a New Beginning.*
Winchester: O Books

Firlik, K. (2007) *Another Day in the Frontal Lobe: A Brain Surgeon Exposes Life on the Inside.* New York: Random House Trade Paperbacks

Kemp, M. (2000) *The Autobiography of Martin Kemp TRUE.*
Birmingham: Orion.

Persaud, Dr. Raj (2006) *The Motivated Mind.* New York City:
Bantam Paperbacks

Brain & Spine Foundation (2023)
Available at: www.brainandspine.org.uk (Accessed: 22 April 2023)

Brain Aneurysm Foundation (2023) Available at: www.bafound.org
(Accessed 3 May 2023)

Care Opinion (Sept. 2022) Available at: www.careopinion.org.uk
(Accessed: 3 May 2023)

Headway – the brain injury association (2023)
Available at: www.headway.org.uk (Accessed: 22 April 2023)

Organ Donation Scotland (2021) Available at: www.organdonation.scot
(Accessed: 22 April 2023)

Please, remember to look me up on facebook
and leave a review/like/share.

You are invited to continue your connection to
NUDGED... by heading over to the below:

Karen Steven Music | Facebook

- Share your thoughts about NUDGED... and see what others think.

- Communicate with the author.

- Find out about talks/Q&As - Recitals

- Please, like, if you feel inclined, and share.

To order further copies of NUDGED...A journey... please visit:
www.karensteven.co.uk

Proceeds from the sale of the book have been made to

Bignold Ward, Caithness General Hospital

&

Palliative Care, Dunbar Hospital, Thurso

where my dad, Eion Steven was cared for
August - December 2021.